D1645396

THE SCIENCE MYTH

Also by Magnus Pyke

NOTHING LIKE SCIENCE
SLAVES UNAWARE?

Magnus Pyke

THE SCIENCE MYTH

Illustrated by
MICHAEL FFOLKES

JOHN MURRAY
FIFTY ALBEMARLE STREET LONDON

© *Magnus Pyke 1962*

Printed in Great Britain by
Butler & Tanner Ltd, Frome and London

To Guy Boas, Sir Jack Drummond and my Wife

by all of whom I have been moulded

this book is affectionately dedicated

CONTENTS

The idea for this book was first explored in an essay called 'Procrustes and his Scientific Bedstead', published in The Listener. *The Editor's opportune encouragement is gratefully acknowledged.*

M. P.

PROCRUSTES AND HIS
SCIENTIFIC BEDSTEAD

THE GREEK fable of Procrustes tells of a robber who compelled those of the public coming within his reach to conform
to an average. His method was to put each of them as he came
into a bed—the same bed for all. Those who were too tall were
cut down to size. Those who fitted exactly were allowed to go
scot free.

Now this gruesome story describes a state of affairs that
exists today. The rigid structure of life in a modern industrial
society—in which everyone is caught up—brings discomfort
or injury to all those who deviate from the average. Dickens
mentioned one early aspect of the Procrustean principle in the
distribution of postmen's uniforms—'made by contract—no
measuring—mysterious dispensations of Providence—all the
short men get long coats—all the long men short ones.' In just
the same way, the supreme achievements of scientific technology—the family car, the television set and the programme
it shows, the prefabricated house and the durable consumer
goods in it—all must be standard articles, mass produced
for 'the average consumer'. Unfortunately, there are a great
many people who deviate from the average. A correspondent
once wrote a letter to *The Times* pointing out with regret that
half the schoolchildren in London have an intelligence
quotient below the average.

But the progress of mass-production and automation, the
dwindling size of the world resulting from the extension of
communication and information, the increasing noisiness, and
the rate at which things are happening press more and more
insistently on the citizen of today.

The Procrustean bed pinches the nonconformist in small

ways as well as big. To take an example, in the United States the whole great weight of the industrial and social machine compels a man to enjoy massive technological comforts of the most diverse sorts—even if he is smothered in the attempt. And of all the amenities, the most lavish and the most characteristic is the American bathroom. In the American bathroom, where Mr Edmund Wilson claims to have had 'more uplifting thoughts, creative and expansive visions' than in the cathedrals of Europe, it is almost obligatory to submit to a shower. The bath itself, in these bathrooms, has been reduced to little more than a vestigial relic. There may be people —indeed, it is certain that there are—who do not enjoy the preliminary blast of freezing cold water, who suffer from the worrying struggle to adjust the valve to maintain a due balance between this and scalding heat, who are incapable of carrying out a significant proportion of their washing while standing on one leg; in short who desire to be relaxed and soothed and soaked rather than stimulated and braced. Yet in the great cities of America the pressure of public opinion, transmitted through the subtle atmosphere of social conformity as well as by way of the accepted codes for builders and plumbers, insists that everybody except the most strong-minded eccentrics *must* accept a shower rather than a bath.

Similar minor examples are to be found in any technologically advanced country. Although the British climate is not particularly warm, there are periods in the summer when the sun shines and the atmosphere becomes both hot and humid. The British have a saying that thunder turns milk sour because in pre-technological times there was no way to keep the milk cool. Today, half a dozen great electrical firms use their formidable powers of persuasion to press the citizens to install refrigerators. But when the people conform—as conform they must—they are compelled to get down on their knees in order to put away the butter. The architect of Napoleon's tomb in the Invalides in Paris compels every visitor to bow when he looks at the monument of the great emperor. The force of mass-production causes every user to stoop when he goes to a British refrigerator, in which the first shelf is customarily arranged within inches of the floor.

But these are small things, you will say. A man can think great thoughts, and love, and eat, and talk, and attain his full free stature even if he has a bathroom shower imposed on him, and a television set, ball-point pens, a deep-freeze, an electrically operated tin-opener, two motorcars and a long-playing record-player that never leaves off. The big limitation of the scientific bedstead with which we have to come to terms or else suffer damage is industrialisation. It is from factory industries that the main impact of science is derived.

Most people would say they are happier sleeping in a bed than on the floor, and there can be no doubt that the scientific technology which made possible the steam engine and the spinning jenny and the power loom, and now gives us atomic energy and the electronic computer, has vastly increased the sum total of this kind of human happiness. But the cost has been high: Procrustes has captured us. And the initial mutilations from the newly designed bed that he made for us were very severe. It may have been dull in times past for women to be compelled to spend much of their time spinning—and the pre-technological highborn ladies and servant girls were alike all spinsters because hand spinning and textile manufacture were slow operations—but at least it was not painful. When the new kind of world began, in which we are obliged to live today, the compulsory change from a domestic occupation to a technological industry caused a good deal of pain all round.

There are two different things that we shall need to discuss more than once as we go along. First: what kind of a bed it is in which we have been trapped. In the early eighteenth century in the English Midlands it began as a machine with 250 spindles for spinning cotton, and it was activated by a donkey; next it was John Kay's mechanical weaving machine, then those of Arkwright and Hargreaves; by the end of the century there were great textile factories with steam engines to work the machines. The shape of the bed—this is one side of the question. But secondly, what makes our scientific Procrustes do it? Why suddenly does he take it into his head, in 1760 or thereabouts, to lie in wait and rob people of their rural freedom and compel them to submit to his bed? Textile machinery was not newly invented in the eighteenth century: Leonardo da Vinci worked out the design of a perfectly satisfactory spinning machine and made detailed drawings of it in the sixteenth —but nobody did anything about it for two hundred years. As for the steam engine, Hero of Alexandria made one as a toy in the second century B.C. Besides knowing how to construct the technological bed, clearly there also has to be the will to use it. Why did this will only appear in 1760?

In prehistoric times man won a modest victory over darkness by inventing the means of controlling fire to give him light for simple lamps at night. He became used to this degree of illumination. The great men of Classical and Biblical times, the heroes of history, the painters and musicians and seers did their work and lived their lives in daylight or lamp-light until in 1816 or thereabouts Samuel Clegg lit a London street with gaslight. Procrustes was on the prowl again. 'London is now to be lit during the winter months with the same coal-smoke that turns our winter days into night,' wrote Sir Walter Scott. The *Kölnische Zeitung* of 28 March 1819 at once saw the troubles ahead and, in its systematic Teutonic way, opposed the innovation:

> *On juridical grounds;* because the cost of lighting is to be raised by indirect taxation. Why should any man pay for an installation that is indifferent to him, since it brings him no advantage or even annoys him in certain respects. *On medical grounds;* gas vapours have an injurious effect on the health of weakly and nervous persons, besides which gas encourages many illnesses by making it easier for people to stay out in the streets, so that they catch colds, coughs and

'... **Hero** of *Alexandria made one as a toy* ...'

sore throats. *On police grounds;* it makes the horse timid and the thief bold . . .*

and so on.

The tortures of the new framework into which industrial man was being compelled to fit himself were not accepted without a struggle. The Luddites of 1811 mounted a direct frontal attack and led by 'King Ludd' they smashed up the new textile machinery, striking by night and masked like an English version of the Ku Klux Klan. But Procrustes could cope with this sort of thing. How were the workmen of Nottingham and Yorkshire, Lancashire, Derbyshire and Leicestershire to know that he was a mythical being, a thing of the spirit and too strong to be defeated with hammers and pickaxes. The next year they were shot down by authority and 'King Ludd' was killed. Not even Byron's oratory in the House of Lords could protect the handicraftsmen from the new conditions of industrial Britain to which they had to conform. A batch of hangings and transportations in 1813 lopped off the rest of the recalcitrant members who had not fitted into the bed—and the thing was done.

Direct resistance to the technological environment has been tried on a number of occasions and has not been entirely abandoned even now. Beside the textile workers, the lamplighters too, in their small way, tried to keep things as they were and refused to light the new-fangled gas lamps. Again the inexorable progress of the railway lines was resisted in a number of quarters; some landowners refused the right of way. To this day the telegraph poles by the line at Dingistow in Monmouthshire are only two feet high so that they should not spoil the view from the big house. At Oxford, the railway station is half an hour's brisk walk from the centre of the city because the prominent inhabitants refused to have it any nearer. Nevertheless, the framework of the technological society was

* From *Inventors of our World*, by Joachim Leithauser, translated by Michael Bullock. (Weidenfeld and Nicolson, 1958.)

completed. Even if the man with the red flag walked in front of the horseless carriage for only a day in history before he was swept away, he did have his day. Even now newspaper printers and typesetters hold back the introduction of new machines, cigarette workers delay the introduction of new devices, dockers put as many men on the ships as if fork-lift trucks had never been heard of. But we know that their resistance is in vain: Procrustes can deal with them.

The scientific bed caused a lot of pain when it was being constructed. Factories run by steam engines brought workpeople from the country and crowded them together in great towns such as Manchester, which was still in the early nineteenth century run like the collection of rural villages it once had been. Outbreaks of typhus, cholera and smallpox wiped out child apprentices in thousands. Unguarded shafts and pulleys killed and injured the children and adults alike. Lead poisoning, anthrax and rickets were only some of the injuries inflicted on the community by the new way of technological living. Back-to-back houses and 'gin palaces' changed the face of the land in towns and mining villages alike.

In the fable of Procrustes it was the hero, Theseus, who eventually slew the robber and freed the road so that travellers could pass on their way without contorting themselves into the frame that had been set up for them. There have been many heroes who have succeeded in curbing the depredations of the Procrustes of the modern world. In 1802 the British Parliament passed the Health and Morals of Apprentices Act, and in 1833 the first Factory Act protected children between the ages of 9 and 13 years to the extent of insisting that they should attend school for two hours a day. Chadwick in 1842 advanced the cause of public sanitation in his report, 'The Sanitary Condition of the Labouring Population'. The Mines and Colleries Act prohibited the employment of women and young children underground in the pits. In 1847 the gallant Lord Shaftesbury, after a battle lasting fourteen years to ameliorate the rigours of factory work for children, succeeded in persuading Parliament to pass the Ten Hours Act.

'History', wrote Gibbon, '. . . is, indeed, little more than the register of the crimes, follies and misfortunes of mankind.' He also wrote, 'It might perhaps be more conducive to the virtue as well as the happiness of mankind, if all possessed the necessaries and none the superfluities of life.' But though he wrote at length about *what* happened he never attempted to determine *why* it took place. He looked back to the early days of the republic of Rome, when life was simple and virtuous, and then turned with disgust to see the later effects of luxury acquired from the hard work and good government of such simpler days. We in our modern twentieth-century times accept Gibbon's first pessimistic statement no more than did his contemporaries. As for his second point, we can now arrange, can we not, by the new scientific technology we have invented, that all shall possess the superfluities of life as well as the necessities.

Few would deny that we want to live the rich, soft life that our technical abilities allow. We must pass along the path where Procrustes lies in wait. The cheap and excellent textiles; plentiful soap and modern detergents; electricity for power and, above all, for light at night; dyes and flavours, drugs and anaesthetics that lift the dark load of fear and pain and death itself; steel and chrome, aluminium—a rare curiosity fifty years ago—metals of all sorts; and the strange new 'plastics', better than anything known to nature, strong, malleable, beautiful; all these we could not give up. Gandhi wanted to lead the Indians along another road, to simple peasant industry, home-spun cloth, goats' milk, virtue and great thoughts, but few would follow. We are determined to go along the way past the house of Procrustes.

We have learned a great deal about how to cope with the situation since the shootings and hangings of 1813. We have seen Procrustes for what he is and have forced him to make the scientific bed less excruciating to sleep in. The Factory Acts protect the victims against the worst ravages of tuberculosis, pneumoconiosis (by which name the dust diseases of industry are more technically described), weaver's tooth, lead poisoning, and mechanical injury. And even though it may not be everyone's choice to spend a major part of the day doing tedious work in a noisy factory, at least the hours of labour are restricted (or if they are not, the victim stays willingly in bed because he knows that he is being richly paid at 'time-and-a-half' or 'double-time' rate to do so), the factory is warm, and music is piped into the working space to distract and charm him just as it is in a restaurant to divert the diner's attention from the clattering of tools there.

The second lesson is one learned direct from Gibbon. After commenting on the dangers to virtue and happiness arising from the desire for the superfluities of life, he goes on:

> But in the present imperfect condition of society, luxury, though it may proceed from vice or folly, seems to be the only means that can correct the unequal distribution of property. The diligent mechanic and the skilful artist, who have obtained no share in the division of the earth, receive a voluntary tax from the possessors of land; and the latter are prompted by a sense of interest, to improve those estates, with whose produce they may purchase additional pleasures.

We can hope that the modern luxuries for the possession of which we are prepared to suffer so much do not proceed from vice. But since in the modern world we all want to possess them, we had to learn how to make it possible by high wages and hire purchase for everyone to do so. Thus the desire to go along the way that leads past Procrustes is now general. The Luddites hated the new automatic textile machinery installed by their masters: the automobile workers love their automated assembly lines. Their preoccupation is to make sure that after suffering in the factory they are themselves able to buy enough of the automobiles they make. This second lesson is, therefore, that everyone in the community must *want* to take the road that passes by the scientific bed and the most direct way to make them do so is to give them their full share in the wealth of things that science brings.

The third lesson is to study how best to sleep in the bed in comfort even if it does not, in actual fact, fit our human anatomy and disposition. After all, a man put to ride a horse for the first time finds it an uncomfortable and hazardous method of locomotion but he can quickly learn to ride. The mutilations resulting from his excursions in equitation may be of minor significance, insufficient to affect his happiness; little harm is done by the fracture of a few collar-bones, and the development of bow legs from prolonged riding is a trivial matter. The number of people killed by being thrown from their mounts in the days of the horse was no greater in proportion than those killed in motorcars today—and they are a small price to pay for the benefits of mechanised locomotion.

The pioneer of the modern industrial environment was Henry Ford. His travelling belt brought wealth and happiness. His motto, 'Buy a Ford, your wife can drive it, any colour you like so long as it's black', is the touchstone of the world today, standardisation being an essential feature of this rich modern epoch. Henry Ford applied on a large scale to the processes of technology Adam Smith's doctrine of the division of labour. The people who had to work the system, however, could not divide themselves up small enough and the results were shown by Charlie Chaplin in 'Modern Times'. The little men servicing the lines of moving parts jerked and shook and screwed and hammered themselves to pieces.

Today we have managed to a large extent to prevent the work of the factory so pressing on the men who do it that they cannot stop themselves from continuing the paralytic movements of their working hours while they eat and sleep. This has been done partly by practice. If a man uses a hammer long enough he learns eventually not to hit his thumb. If he uses a pneumatic drill all day long he finds some way not to go on shaking when he gets home. Girls who worked in the deafening noise of the Lancashire cotton mills acquired the ability to communicate with each other by lip reading.

The next step, of course, is to invent a system of industrial training by which a man new to the Procrustean bed can be taught to adapt himself to sleep in it without harm. This system may be simple or complex. It may merely involve impressing on the worker the importance of always using a new spanner, the jaws of which are true and undamaged, or it may comprise a complex series of instructions to insure that an elaborate machine shall not blast him with steam or cut him to pieces.

But the injury that a working man suffers within the confines of the modern technological system may not be restricted to physical damage: it may also harm his mind. The scientists and technologists live happy and creative lives. The organic chemist of the nineteenth century who stimulated the tar distiller to distil tar to provide the phenols and cresols and naphthols from which the new dyes and drugs and flavours and scents and detergents and chemical reagents could be synthesised was a happy god. Such a man was creating beauty and health and riches and, above all, enjoying the intellectual achievement of creation and discovery. He was, indeed, a brother to Procrustes himself, who built the factories. But other men were compelled to work in them, and not all these men were happy even after the dark poisonous smoke of the tar distillery, and the smell of the dye works, and the long hours in the stuffy warehouses of the wholesale drug houses had been done away with by Clean Air Regulations and Factory Acts.

Industrial training schemes are aimed to protect the worker's mind from harm as well as his body. Just as a short man is more comfortable than a tall one in a short bed, in the same way, a less intellectually inclined person fits more happily into a dull repetitive job than does someone of an intellectual bent. But even so, no matter how carefully they are selected, even unintellectual workers may get bored and discontented and careless. Industrial training for foremen will therefore include instruction on how to deal with the minds of operatives filling bottles with aspirin tablets or screwing on telephone mouthpieces so that they do not become discontented and unhappy. The technique of how this can be done is as yet in its infancy. The best way to make people doing dull work happy is to let them know that the work they are doing is important and that the people for whom they are doing it care about them. Even if it is not true, the scientific bed may at least seem to be more comfortable to the worker in the aspirin factory if the well-trained foreman tells him that the managing director depends on his personal co-operation and (after referring to his notebook) asks after his wife's rheumatism.

I have described elsewhere a famous research carried out by the Western Electric Company, where elaborate scientific observations were made on the behaviour of a group of women who were assembling electrical components. This was the Hawthorn Experiment. The result of the research was that where nutrition and physiology, work study, time-and-motion investigations, lighting, ventilation and acoustics were all applied in vain to increase the productivity of the team, the simple human fact that a whole lot of serious-minded people were interested in them as individuals caused the women to make so enthusiastic an effort that their output became consistently better than that of the rest of the factory.

The scientific bed in the form that it strikes many ordinary people seems to be an inhuman sort of thing. This is odd because it is, in fact, entirely of human manufacture. If, therefore, it presses on the minds of the factory workers who are in it, it is entirely right and proper that their minds should be relieved. These workers are human beings and an adroit reassurance on this point now and again is eminently to be encouraged. The chosen instrument may be a device in 'man management' elaborated by the training section of the firm, or it may be a jolly works outing to the seaside, or an office party at which the managing director is brought round at the precise moment when the workers have drunk sufficient to make them cheerful and friendly and receptive to the use of their Christian names and yet, at the same time, not too cheerful and outspoken. These are nowadays well-recognised processes of the industrial system.

Nevertheless, the system can be extended in all directions. The lesson learned from the elaborate, expensive and prolonged Hawthorn Experiment—that people fit more happily into the technological environment and their minds are calmer if they are noticed—has been well learned. The money spent on it was not wasted. Not only do the people responsible for the operatives who assemble the electrical components take care to notice them now, but the senior officials who manage the foremen take notice of them too. They send them Christmas cards (provided by the firm). And right up to the top, sleep in the bed is made more tranquil by big desks, and personal assistants, and flattering and euphonious titles.

Learning to live within the machinery of scientific life is one way to avoid being harmed by science. Training in how to handle tools and machinery, in how to deal with high-voltage transformers, learning how not to be run down and killed by motorcars, or driven into nervous frustration by the tintinnabulations of too many transistorised radios is part of the matter. And knowing how to stave off the frustrations of an employment which is merely an unsatisfying gap in the kind of activity a man really wants to do when his 'employment' is over for the day is another. This is an urgent problem and the Hawthorn solution will only answer in certain circumstances. This is the reason why modern industrialists, after having made the scientific environment of their factories as agreeable as they can, after having warmed them and painted them, and trained their workers so well that they could almost do their duties in their sleep, as a last resort make existence in the industrial bed bearable by asking people to stay in it for shorter and shorter periods of time during each working week.

There is, of course, another approach to the problem altogether. It is to compel Procrustes to abandon his normal tyrannical system of behaviour and accept at least the first steps towards democracy. The alternative is to change the bed to fit the man. Whereas a 'training officer' will work out a system by which an operator can watch a dial above his head, compare its reading with a thermometer beside him, work a lever with his left foot, push a plastic cylinder through an opening with his left hand and bring down a lever with his right, all with the greatest ease and the highest efficiency, the 'human engineer' will do nothing of the sort. He will try to design the machine so that the way that comes naturally to the operator is the way it should be worked. Procrustes demands that the locomotive engineer shall stand peering out of his cab on a cold, dark night straining his eyes as he whirls by to catch sight of the appropriate colour signal high up on the gantry. And if he fails to see it and wrecks the train, he is to blame. He has failed to fit himself into the Procrustean bed. The 'human engineer', on the other hand, will make no attempt to force the driver to conform to this harsh ironmongery. He will consider whether the design of the driver's cab is properly suited to his human needs; whether the driver has a wide field of view and can be expected to see the line ahead; whether the signal light is at an appropriate height; whether it is bright enough to be seen; and whether, indeed, a light is the best signal to use at all.

'Human engineering' is something that must be taken seriously nowadays. We had been constructing by our new and increasing mastery of science and technology a world in which it was difficult for us to live without harming ourselves. This world, however, gave us power and wealth and luxury beyond the imaginings of earlier epochs, and at first some measure of deformity seemed a small price to pay. Now, however, by the same process of thinking and experimentation and rational logic which developed the wealth of technology, we are proposing to modify and streamline our surroundings so that we can enjoy the benefits they bring without suffering the mutilations.

Human engineers may study their problems as a whole by studying the whole man and his behaviour; they can also investigate separate parts of the problem one at a time. Consider nutrition, for example. The urban diet eaten by an industrial worker may be unsatisfactory and harmful. The amount of calcium in it, let us say, is inadequate. Because his diet is deficient the industrial worker loses each day more calcium than he gains from his food. The human engineer takes thought so as to be able to improve the situation by improving the diet. Within the half century in which we are now living he has achieved great things in this direction. I remember as a boy seeing in the cotton towns of Lancashire in the north of England operators with bow legs and deformed chests, their stature grotesquely stunted. These were the victims of rickets born of poverty, bad factory conditions, darkness and a shortage of calcium. Human engineering has improved the diet. While they are still infants, the workers can get cod-liver oil, as schoolchildren they drink more milk, and for the whole population 14 ounces of chalk—calcium carbonate of the highest quality—is added to every 280 lbs of flour.

The successes that the human engineer may have achieved must not blind us to the difficulty of his art and the delicacy he requires if he is to exercise it successfully. The average calcium needs of the 'average man' are easily assessed. It is much more difficult to know what an individual working-class baby will want and compare it with what he would get if the human engineer did nothing. And then, when the piece of engineering has been done, and the dried milk is enriched with calciferol and the fish-liver oil concentrate fortified with vitamin D_3, it is harder still to regulate what the baby will actually get. The children of the Lancashire cotton workers no longer suffer from rickets. A remarkable social achievement has been brought about, but to keep the social body in exact adjustment is just as difficult an operation as maintaining the adjustment of a machine. It is possible to provide too much vitamin D and calcium if the human engineer does not watch his indicators.

Then again, the behaviour of the Bantus in South Africa became a source of trouble to the human engineers whose business was food and efficiency. The necessary amounts of calcium in the diet, either from milk or cheese or by way of added chalk in bread, and the proper level of vitamin D to help the calcium act having been worked out at last for working populations in the industrial West, it became apparent that things were different for the Bantus. Not being subjected to the full pressures of civilisation as we are, they have habituated themselves to a different diet. The amount of calcium they eat is small by Western standards but so is the amount they lose. As seen by the human engineer, they can keep in 'calcium balance' without having chalk added to their food.

In the classical legend, the travellers who were too big for the bed were killed by having pieces of themselves chopped off. Today they are compressed into a too-small island, be it Manhattan or Britain, forced together in a semi-recumbent posture in an automobile crowded on to an inadequate road, stupefied by too little spiritual elbow-room at the automated factory by day and by the limitations of the television by night. The pressure of all this can be killing. Yet on the other hand it may be necessary for life. At a recent scientific meeting of the Institute of Biology at which these topics were being discussed, a clinical expert expressed the opinion that the best therapeutic treatment—often, indeed, the only successful treatment—to keep alive a man who after a lifetime of labour as a coal-miner had at last been pensioned off, was to send him down the mine again. The wounds inflicted by his years under restraint as a victim of the scientific bed were so deep that for him retirement was lethal.

But besides being squeezed, modern man is also stretched. He cannot remain quietly at home dealing with such business as may arise. No, he must fly half round the world, to a technical conference in Japan, in Alaska, in Nairobi or Istanbul. Just when he is acclimatised to the hot, busy, restless but luxurious hotel in Chicago, he finds himself consigned to another, equally exhausting to the spirit and equally luxurious, in Manchester, or Melbourne or Milan. For his technical work, the modern manager has no sooner attended a conference in his own country than he must needs fly to another half-way round the world.

Besides being stretched thus to keep abreast of technology and the business of industrial life, the modern man has his spirit stretched to breaking point by knowing not only his own troubles but everyone else's as well. The marvels of the up-to-date system of communications—by telephone, radio, television, through cables, the ether, even bounced off plastic balloons orbiting the globe every hour or so—all these rack his feelings with worries about the disasters of the Congolese, the Finns or the inhabitants of Tierra del Fuego. Nowhere is now too remote to affect his business, his feelings and his happiness.

The moth *Biston betularia* may have something to teach about how best to adjust our lives to the industrial scene. This creature was accustomed to harmonise with the brown trunks of the trees which were its natural habitat. Then came industrialisation, and the trunks of the trees were no longer brown but black from the smoke of the factories and furnaces. Procrustes once again demanded a mutilation (or at least a change) as the price of survival. As the factories continued to darken the country, *Biston betularia* became extinct and a new black strain, *Biston betularia carbonaria*, took their place.

Who knows whether man has already changed his coat like *Biston betularia*, and if so, what he has lost in the process? Why is it that rats and mice and blackbeetles and raucous, scolding starlings can adjust themselves so quickly and comfortably to what appear to many of us to be the less attractive features of industrial civilisation, while gracious and timid creatures gradually die away? Is there somewhere a strain of gracious and attractive men capable of thriving in a technological climate and making it gracious and attractive too? Can we safely leave this to happen eventually or must we help it along? And if we need to give things a push in the right direction, how shall we go about it?

2

SHORT CUT OR LONG
STRETCH?

I ONCE knew a man who was able for quite some time to dine
out on the question: 'What is the use of an Englishwoman?'
Obviously, there is a variety of possible answers to this query
suited to a variety of different audiences. The official reply,
however, is that the main purpose of an Englishwoman is to
maximise industrial exports to the dollar area.

The question is not as frivolous as it looks nor, indeed, is the
answer as far-fetched as it seems. In simpler terms, the question
asks what a modern, up-to-date, industrial community is trying to achieve. Industrial man likes to see an efficient, well-run,
tidy and punctual world. No matter how rich and prosperous
his country is, he wants to see it richer and more prosperous.
No industrial plant can ever be permitted to stand still, it must
get bigger, its capital investment must become larger, the
number of branch depots it controls must increase, its exports
spread more widely round the world and the number of its
vice-presidents proliferate without end. And each consumer
must possess two cars, a deep-freeze, and television sets, nylon
shirts and plastic fishing rods without number. It is for all
these that he is prepared to suffer the tensions of industrial
employment; it is on this basis the patriotic Englishwoman
dedicates her life.

One day it may be possible to delineate the target, to see the
goal we are aiming at. There was once a saying that 'a man
cannot wear more than one pair of pants at a time'. This is
demonstrably untrue. But we can suppose that half a dozen
pairs of pants will be about enough. At the moment, however,
the target number of cars and planes and goods of all sorts is
quite obscure. No sooner has the 'standard of living', as it is

technically called, been doubled than there is an urgent cry to double it again. It is because of all this that the efficient life has become accepted as synonymous with the good life. And to attain efficiency, men have been willing to drill themselves to the rigours of modern living.

It is part of the accepted dogma of life in an industrial society that employment in industry is a good thing. In spite of the efforts made by employees to work for a shorter and shorter proportion of each period of seven revolutions of the earth on its axis, there is no doubt that to be employed provides the worker with an essential measure of social prestige and satisfaction. It is for this reason that young people hasten to leave school at the earliest age permitted to them and enter industrial employment. The material reward their wages will bring is only one of the reasons that drives them on. Social and family tradition and the busy rushing mood of the present age also prompt them. To many adolescents, work offers relief from the boredom of the back streets, from the routine of school and the restrictions attached to the status of a pupil. *What* they do in the factory is of less importance than that they are there; the social significance of work is greater than the nature of the work itself.

The change from the routine of school to that of work is profound. This is the first step along the road that leads to the modern state. At school, learning is pursued for its own sake, and success is judged by attainments directly related to learning what is taught. At school, success is judged and acclaimed in terms of work, whereas in industrial life this is not so. Work seldom seems to the worker to have meaning or worth; long hours of dull effort are called for and achievement is judged by the wage-packet, which may have no relation to the difficulty of the work. When he was at school, the young initiate to industry could talk about things that directly interested him and in which he was concerned as a person—football, baseball, cricket, swimming, the school play, who was likely to be top, how the school was doing in competition with other schools.

At work, this is replaced by gossip about time-wasting amusements in which none of the talkers plays any part himself, except perhaps by betting. It is small wonder that the adolescent finds his fresh and natural ingenuousness becoming bruised and tarnished. The first mutilation that he suffers in becoming acclimatised is when he escapes from the monotony of work into a dreamland of fantasy or an artificial attachment to purposeless amusements. At the sound of the hooter he, and a multitude of others who have already fallen victim to the same process, are disgorged from the factory to sports, games, cinemas and dances whose sole purpose is to consume time until the coming of sleep and the next day's employment.

Quis custodes ipsos custodet, that is to say, if the people who run the industries do not really know why they are doing so, and themselves develop gastric ulcers meanwhile, how can we expect them to be able to teach the boys and girls to survive unscathed? The first purpose of industrial training schemes, it can be argued, is to train the newcomers to do their work and to fit in without fuss. If most workers in our world of scientific technology have the attitude that work is a means of making money and that leisure is a method of spending it, why should industrial training aim to do any more than teach the adolescents that this is so, even if it brings satisfaction and purpose neither in work nor play?

The young worker, unmarked by the scars the older ones have almost forgotten, throws a vivid flash of light on the world of modern industry. Dr Lloyd Davies made a study from which he found that the majority of girls and boys go blindly to their fate. They take a job in a factory just because some friend or acquaintance has told them 'it's nice', or that 'it's a good firm'. He asked a group of boys and girls to arrange twelve different factors in order of the importance they attached to them in choosing to dedicate their working lives to one industry rather than another. The girls chose as the first reason for their choice good lavatories. The boys, though they would welcome promotion, wanted security. Must we believe that at the outset of their lives in this exciting climate of scientific advance, Procrustes has with a single blow lopped off adventurousness, creativeness, poetry, the martyr's crown, risk, chance and invention, so that the young apprentice in taking his first job has his eyes fixed on his old-age pension?

When they take their first steps along the road that leads to the world of adult life, the young workers still trail some of the clouds of glory from their unregenerate and unindustrial childhood. Before industrial training has had a chance to mould them, adolescent employees in factories have a tendency to lark about. They exhibit curiosity to know what would happen if they pushed their hand in under a machine guard or squirted a jet from a compressed-air hose at a passing friend. They are bold and foolhardy. These characteristics must be knocked out of them if they are to take an adult place in a well-run workshop. Until they have been trained *not* to show curiosity, foolhardiness, boldness and playfulness they will fall too easy victims to the dangers that surround them. In other words, these attributes lead directly to industrial accidents.

They must be trained and they must learn to accept this training that is designed to rid them of their natural spontaneity. It is not always a pleasant process. The sickness-absence rate is a measure of social health and of the emotional and mental adjustment to industrial work and the circumstances of work. We must not be surprised, therefore, that the sickness-absence rate of adolescents is the highest of any age group except that of old men just before retirement.

The first stage of industrial training is to knock out of the ingenuous adolescent all the 'nonsense' of the young, this being most of his or her eagerness and ingenuousness. This is the first blow struck by modern circumstance to get the juvenile worker to grow up into an industrial adult who will fit the needs of the times. Industrial training schemes, however, go further than this. Careful and scientific thought has been given to ways of moulding and forcing workers to fit well and to fit quickly. At one time, the novice had to do the best he could to avoid the cruder mutilations of industrial accidents—or getting the sack. Those were the days when the apprentice was left to fend for himself or, at least, given the opportunity of changing himself by the process known technically as 'sitting by Nellie'. That is to say, he was expected to pick up the rules of the industrial world by watching and imitating an experienced worker who, as the kindly but expressive saying is, had already 'been through the mill' himself.

Now, however, university professors of Engineering Production or of Industrial Psychology have thought out the whole business. First of all, the trainee is taught what it is that has to be done. This does not mean that he is told that he is to make a pair of boots, or to contribute to the construction of an aeroplane, or to the making of a fertiliser to feed the starving millions of the world. What he is taught is that *this* goes in here and that *that* comes across there, and that *then* he is to press the pedal *there* and pull the knob painted green until the plunger drops down.

Up-to-date scientific methods of training require the instructor to show his pupil the exact pattern of movement that makes up the separate stages of an operation. The learner is then expected to practice each of these separate steps until he knows them. Only then will the teacher allow him to put them together and carry out the manœuvre as a whole. Of course, when he first does this he does it slowly and deliberately. He is like a man who has just learnt to drive a car but who still has to think what to do at each stage—'Now I must put the brake on; now the clutch must be pushed in (Oh dear! I ought to have taken my foot off the accelerator first)'—and so on. Even to get so far with the training of an industrial worker, a lot of heavy scientific thinking has had to be done by the specialists. The young student who has come so lightheartedly from school to do a job and earn his living is, in fact, being moulded to use his eyes and ears—a good engineer listens to the note his machine is making—his sense of touch, yes, and his sense of smell as well. And not only does the modern science of industrial psychology and engineering production take anxious thought to train the five senses of the boys and girls who are to be moulded, it also deals equally scientifically with the 'sixth sense' that, up till the present, we may have considered as a special gift possessed by a few skilled people. This quality is now called the 'kinaesthetic sense'. It is the way—and I quote an official publication of the U.K. Department of Scientific and Industrial Research—'through which information is transmitted to the brain from nerve endings in the muscles, tendons and joints and whereby knowledge is given of the position and speed of movement of a limb, and of the pressure exerted by the muscles.'

Quite soon, under the influence of industrial training, the unregenerate boy or girl who came from school quite raw is changed into a trained factory worker who knows what moves of his hands and feet to make, and who has practised the sequence of operations he has to do as a whole. Sensation, decision and action come to overlap each other, hesitations are eliminated; while the limbs are performing one movement, the senses and the brain are preparing the next. Soon ultimate success is reached, 'attention becomes free in the final stage . . . to pursue outside interests, like the knitter who reads while she knits'. The first goal of industrial training has been achieved. The worker can now do his duty without conscious thought and, furthermore, unlike the knitter he does *not* read while he works.

But scientific training for industry has gone further than this. The people who are doing the training seek out a worker who can already do the job. They then write down on a 'sensori-meter process chart' everything he does, make a note of everything he looks at, even record everything he thinks—for example, when a pointer moves to a particular place on a dial, does the man have to *think* whether he must next move a lever to the left or to the right? Or when he has soldered a wire to a terminal, does he have to make up his mind whether the wire is properly stuck or not? Next, when they have fully scrutinised the already skilled operator, the training experts study the job to see whether it is not possible to change it round so that the things the worker has to look at may be more easily seen and the things he has to do more easily done. More important still, having discovered the occasions when the skilled man has to make up his mind, the experts try to arrange things so that in the future the new man never shall have to make a decision, and shall never have to rely on his memory, and indeed be able to do his simpler task without conscious volition or the need for thought at all.

When the work has been streamlined to this extent, study is made to see how the people who are to do it can most expeditiously be taught to do it quickly. And here again it has been shown that 'sitting by Nellie'—which, of course is a succinct if impolite way of describing most traditional systems of apprenticeship—is not a good method of teaching. A quick, efficient industrial worker, moulded for the life he has to lead— of accident-free, smoothly executed operations—can most rapidly be produced if he or she practises first one part of a task, then a contiguous portion, and then another, until at last, like a juggler on the stage, he can do the whole thing with swift effortless virtuosity—and without thinking.

Although this sort of operation, in which the technological man or woman is softly and persistently hammered into shape until—Pinnocchio in reverse—from being a living creature he becomes for forty hours a week an insensate puppet, represents a remarkable achievement of the moulding process, there is still more to come. This is the penultimate stage in a process that began a century and a half ago. Richard Oastler could write to the *Leeds Mercury* of 29 September 1830 thus:

> Thousands of little children, both male and female, but principally female, from seven to fourteen years of age, are daily compelled to labour from six o'clock in the morning to seven in the evening, with only—Britons, blush while you read it—with only thirty minutes allowed for eating and

recreation. Poor infants . . . and when your joints can act no longer, your emaciated frames are cast aside, the boards on which you lately toiled and wasted life away are instantly supplied with other victims, who in this boasted land of liberty are *hired*—not sold—as slaves and daily forced to hear that they are free. . . .'

That was when industrialisation was new and applied science just beginning. That was when it was first discovered that these admirable things could also be hurtful. Today, the grosser damage is no longer seen; the injury is more subtle. Even the training programme that prepares a man or woman to perform a task effortlessly, comfortably and almost mindlessly—a task that reduces a man or woman almost to the status of a machine—even this gentle process has been circumvented by replacing man or woman *by* a machine. Automation has appeared.

The training and forming of men and women to fit the requirements of production technology are not painful to everyone. There are people who fit into industrial life without a pang. They positively enjoy the rhythmic demands of the machines and processes they serve; they take pride in the skill with which they solder the insides of television sets, weave carpets, or machine the armholes in singlets. Although routine employment in industrial production may not always be bad, automation, it seems, is better. Joan Woodward, lecturer in Industrial Sociology at Oxford University, made a study of employment relations. In this she found that to the extent that mass-production operations gave way to more advanced levels of technology and automation requiring the intelligent control of large plants, so did the operators abandon their customary habits of slipping away to the lavatory for a smoke and eagerly awaiting the hooter that was going to release them. Instead, the 'situation demands' of their increased responsibility 'create conditions conducive to human happiness'.

Of course, the substitution of automation for work previously done with hand tools does not do away altogether with stresses and strains on the people in factories. Instead of becoming practised craftsmen trained to carry out a series of manual operations at maximum speed on the things that come past them, they now must be turned into 'mental craftsmen'. Now the training officers begin to talk about the 'mental load' that complicates the relationship between what the man sees and what he does. If ever the industrial production upon which we modern men depend for our textiles that never wear out, for the drugs that are to keep us in constant health, for the vehicles that allow us to move from one place to another faster and faster in ever increasing comfort—if ever it develops into complete automation, the pressures then will be those that so far only afflict hereditary millionaires. Meanwhile, however, the attendant in a partially automated factory has his troubles, just as he did before when he worked at the travelling belt of a mass-production manufactory of automobile engines.

A. T. Welford, who directed a research on the ergonomics of automation for the British Department of Scientific and Industrial Research, has described some of the troubles that can afflict a man in an automated factory. He cannot continue to be the full man he was when he was eating his breakfast at home but must become instead a 'communication channel' taking in information from the dials and charts and pointers, the winking lights and the hooters round about him and converting it into action to guide the behaviour of the almost sentient factory. And it is not enough for the instruments he watches to show him that everything is going right by not sending out a warning signal. The man may worry over the possibility that the warning signal has failed, and even if the warning signal does not fail, he may become even more anxious over the thought that it *might* do so. And this, says Mr Welford, may destroy his confidence. Even when long experience would seem to have shown him every different way in which the automated machinery under his control can possibly go wrong, and at the same time have let him see how to put things right, this may not restore his confidence. Now he knows what a lot of possible ways there are for things to break down, and the longer he stays in the job, the greater his anxiety becomes and the more unwilling he is to continue. It is all very well for an operator at a lathe to cope with the hazard of spoiling the piece of work on which he is engaged; for the man at the instrument console of an automated factory the 'mental load' of knowing that one wrong decision will bring a whole plant to a shuddering halt can become quite unbearable.

This is the situation of the present time: for some people, the long stretch each day of practical, skilled but mindless work, even in a clean warm and gaily painted factory, squeezes up their natural personality. For others, keeping watch over the dials and pointers and winking lights and the rising and falling of the pens on the automatic charts gradually becomes a torture. Always in the background is the terrible fear that the alarm bell hanging poised above the suave faces of all those dials will one day shatter the purposeful silent hum and shriek out that something has gone wrong.

The human engineer can be very subtle. When he finds, for example, that the operator controlling the dials of an almost automatic machine becomes bored and allows his attention to wander, he can improve the running of the plant and at the same time make the man happier by building into the back of the control panel a device that makes a few of the indicators move one way or the other from time to time, regardless of what is actually happening inside the machine. This gives the operator something to do.

Consider a remarkable piece of human engineering that was worked out by two investigators called Balding and Hatch. They studied the problem of men employed in a steel works where the conditions were very hot. One particular task could have been done by one man in 30 minutes—had the environment not been so hot that a man could only tolerate it for $7\frac{1}{2}$ minutes without collapsing. The straightforward approach would have been to keep him at the job as long as he could stand it and then employ another man. Balding and Hatch did in fact make a very thorough study of what happened to the men as they struggled through their work in front of the furnaces. As they gradually flagged in their labours—'heat stress' is the technical term—their hearts beat faster and faster. So the two investigators reached the scientific conclusions that 'on humanitarian and economic grounds' it was advisable to allow the men to come away from the heat and rest as soon as the rate at which their hearts were beating had increased by 45 beats per minute. The whole thing was worked out very scientifically. A formula was elaborated by which the 'heat stress index', HSI, could be deduced and it was estimated that most people could tolerate an HSI of 30, although very fit, strong men could still go on when their HSI was as high as 60. From this an expression was elaborated by means of which the time, tw, during which an individual could be expected to work in the hot conditions, and the corresponding time, tr, during which he had to rest and recover in the cool could be calculated. By using this formula it was reckoned that the installation of a shield costing £35 would reduce the fierceness of the heat sufficiently to enable one man to last out long enough to complete the 30 minutes' work. By this means £8000 a year in wages otherwise expended on extra men— each of whom would work for $7\frac{1}{2}$ minutes—would be saved, so that it was worth while making things more comfortable and reducing the rigours of this particular kind of operation. It is interesting to note that the details of this useful and systematic piece of human engineering appeared in 1955 in a publication called 'Heating, Piping and Air Conditioning'.

Human engineering has undoubtedly eased the pressures of technology, both physical and mental, on the people who have to live and work in an environment of applied science and technology. This is not to say that much more could not be done. Mechanical engineers who invent and construct the elaborate machines upon which Western civilisation depends are primarily concerned with machinery. They know the average length of the arms and legs of the men and women who will have to control the machines; good textbooks and journals of engineering now publish anthropometric information of this very sort. But designers are only human and it must be a nuisance, to put it no higher, after overcoming technical and engineering problems of great difficulty, to have to alter the shape and size of the final design just because the man who is to work the engine when it is made is only 5 foot 4 inches tall.

Nevertheless, human engineering does now take account of the strength that a man can comfortably exert on a lever, the most effective way he can use a pedal, and the best way to site dials and recorders so that they can readily be seen. The human engineers work on the minds of the people they are engineering as well as on their bodies. They have found, for example, that the attention of an operator is most directly engaged by a horn when its loudness is at least 10 decibels greater than the background noise. In fact, the information that the horn is intended to give is better conveyed by a bell or some other device that makes an intermittent sound. Perhaps there is a deeper significance than at first appears in the fact that in the technological West the call to prayer is by bells whereas the Eastern summons by the sound of a horn is never heard in paved streets.

Human engineers have also studied how to make the actions that men working machinery have to do be actions that 'come naturally' rather than seem unnatural and have to be learnt. When a hoist is controlled by a lever, it is arranged that the lever shall be moved up when the hoist is to go up, and not the other way round. A more sophisticated discovery is that if the amount of current flowing through a machine is controlled by a knob, it is 'natural' for a man to turn the knob clockwise when he wants more current to flow and anti-clockwise when he wants to shut the current off. Similar thought has been given to switches, but here it is found that it is 'natural' for an Englishman to press a switch *down* when he wants to turn a light on and *up* when he wants to turn it off, whereas an

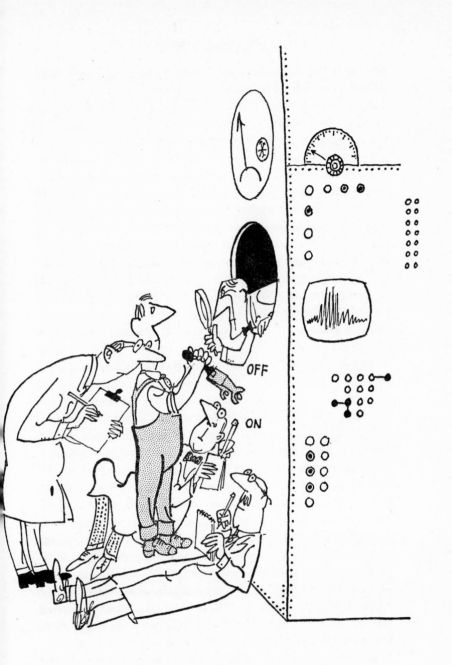

'. . . how to make the actions men have to do come naturally . . .'

American expects the light to go on when he flips the switch *up* and to go out when he moves it *down*.

It can be seen from all this that, in the field of industrial and technological production which is the major preoccupation of the 'advanced' nations of the twentieth century, there are two forces at work on the ordinary human being. On the one hand, the factories and the machines in them demand that the people who serve them shall conform to a specification. They require that men and women shall behave in a certain way and obey certain rules so that the 'gross natural product', based on the wealth of industrial manufacture, shall be large and shall become larger and larger as more up to date and more highly automated equipment is invented and installed. To ensure that the civilised citizens are moulded as quickly and as accurately as possible to the measurements necessary to fit them for their tools, a contingent of highly qualified training officers has come into being.

This is one approach, but on the other hand there is ergonomics, human engineering. The human engineer is a diplomat, not a hero. He does not propose to restrain the factories from springing up and drawing in their quota of men and women. He is fully in favour of their aims to make as many plastic raincoats, automobiles, fertilisers, and antibiotics as efficiently as possible. His object is to sit down and negotiate; to see whether ways can be found of easing the situation; to study, in fact, whether it is not feasible to modify the factories and the machines and processes to fit men and women, rather than making men and women fit them. Mark you, he is not proposing to do away with chemical works and motorcar plants altogether—industrial productivity must go on—but he has, within his terms of reference, done a very great deal. We no longer employ children in cotton mills or women in coal-mines, yet textiles and fuel are produced more efficiently than they were in the middle of the nineteenth century.

In spite of the continuing good work of the human engineers, industrial employment can be painful. It still for most people damages the full human life they could be living. Hours of labour in factories are short and will become shorter; the factories themselves are warm and comfortable; the need for exhausting muscular effort has gone; industrial diseases are no longer a hazard; welfare officers, works canteens, music, sports grounds, pensions, outings to the seaside—these ameliorate the conditions of technological life. Yet the struggle for industrial productivity still imposes the most crippling mutilation of all on the nations who submit themselves to it. Its pursuit makes economic effort the central fact of life on earth and every other human activity peripheral. The central position of work is secured by its uniform duration and timing and by the concentration of work in special places. The main body of the citizenry, the 'workers', are kept segregated from the drones, the women at home, the children, the old and the idle. The complex machinery of industry, the specialisation demanded by the necessary doctrine of the division of labour, make this regimentation necessary. But it has the effect of setting economic effort apart and dividing the day and the week into 'work' and 'everything else'. 'Employment' has a special meaning: it means paid technological work, and all other things are subordinate: social life, conversation, singing and dancing, playing with children or making love. When a man sleeps and eats, whether he tends his garden, his rabbits or his family, whether he attends to his prayers or not, all these are peripheral to 'work'.

But not only is the part of the day devoted to work considered to be more significant than the rest of the twenty-four hours, the working period of life is also assumed to be the part for which all the rest is subsidiary. This way of thinking has so deranged our minds that we have come to accept that only when we are actually carrying out paid industrial work are we serving our purpose on earth. We scarcely know what to do with the earlier and later portions of life. Childhood and youth are segregated from the working years. It is today a crime for a son to help his father, indeed he usually does not know what kind of things his father does at work. Age too is cut off from active 'useful' life by the arbitrary boundary of compulsory retirement. Professor D. W. Harding of London University has seen these happenings very clearly. 'While childhood can be given meaning in terms of our dominant values', he wrote, 'by being viewed as a preparation for "real life", old age is liable to become an apologetic aftermath.' Applied science has given us the 'problem of ageing' by contorting our minds so that, when we are at last released from the need to earn money, we find ourselves believing that the only things seriously worth doing are the things that older people can no longer do. To minds so deformed, the things that 'retired' people do are not considered to be of value. They are empty, merely 'something to do'. The effect of our long-drawn devotion throughout the prime of life to the Sanctity of Technological Employment is frequently fatal and it is a commonplace for men of sixty-five, compulsorily retired and unable themselves to believe in the worth of any non-technological employment, to succumb to apathy and boredom and die.

When at first the citizens of Western civilisations started their march along this path they took the risk in the hope of an ultimate reward of a high material standard of life. They saw ahead, even if a long way off, the glittering prize of wealth and social status and a rich, free, elegant life as a reward for special diligence and effort. In the nineteenth century, scientific technology seemed to offer limitless prospects if they devoted themselves wholeheartedly and exclusively to economic striving. Where Rockefeller and Carnegie and Nobel had attained riches and, presumably, happiness why could not any other man do the same? And so the march along the path began and the long racking years of 'employment' were endured. Things have changed a little in the last hundred years. The ordinary men and women know now that the glittering prize is only a mirage. They march along more from habit than from anything else; we are used to our television sets and electric toasters nowadays. They are not exactly essential to happiness but we should not like to be without them. We still run the risk of suffering harm from using up our lives as we do, but at least the Factory Acts, the Trades Unions and the human engineers have made it less uncomfortable than it once was.

Here and there a few individuals can be found who rebel and refuse to submit to the world of applied science, however comfortable it may now have been made. These are the men who take a week off work to go fishing; the young men who volunteer for climbing expeditions in the Himalayas; the few folk from solid industrious families who become painters or actors; and less desirable Damon Runyon characters who play the horses. Mostly, however, society as a whole submits and suffers the consequences. Even those people who fit in best, the senior technicians and managers, directors on the boards of their companies and vice presidents, these too suffer from the enforced life of scientific technology and economic effort. I am not referring now solely to the physical wounds, the gastric and duodenal ulcers, the coronary heart disease, and the obesity; there is the intellectual and moral suffering as well. The workman at the end of his shift can go home and enjoy some of the natural pleasures of human life. The leisure pursuits of the senior executive tend to be corroded with competitiveness, superficial sociability, display, and conspicuous consumption. He must own a motorcar of a certain size and make, not necessarily to travel in but to prove that he can afford it. He is bound by rule to address his equals on the industrial ladder by their Christian names, to buy them drinks and lunches, and to invite them and their wives to glossy parties, whether he likes them or not. The rigid framework of his position compels him to go to expensive restaurants, to play golf with new and elaborate equipment and to clothe his wife in fashionable costumes and ornaments. When he is eventually released and he 'retires' his lack of money and the loss of his expense account are a serious hurt to him. Throughout his 'working' life, purchasing power has been a direct route to self-esteem, social standing and a relief from the *ennui* of unfilled time. This hollowness of other-than-working activities during his middle life now spreads across the years that are left to him.

The advanced Western nations have bound themselves to their particular system, but there are other ways to live a good life and even to enjoy a reasonable standard of living at the same time. A monarchy may be a good system of government, particularly if the monarch is powerful and successful and brings wealth and prosperity to the populations over which he rules. But if the king begins to become too demanding, if the sacrifices he demands of his subjects begin to encroach too far into the affairs of their domestic human lives, then the material successes of the king may not seem worth having at such high cost. Under these circumstances, a wise nation may wish to retain their monarchy but curb the demands of the monarch lest he became a tyrant.

The British have successfully turned a kingdom into a constitutional monarchy. The Americans, while cleaving to the notion of democracy, do not vote on everything because if they did nothing would get done at all. Now it is up to the nations who have committed themselves to scientific technology as the main source of their wealth and power to temper the rigours of efficiency and productivity so that the good life has a look-in as well.

3

WAR, FORGETFULNESS AND
THE HUMAN BOTTOM

MILITARY TRAINING has throughout history been one of the most effective, as well as the most peculiar, processes by which the human personality becomes pressed into an unnatural shape. The students of laughter have never given any very convincing answer to the question why it is that the sight of *one* grown-up man stiffly jerking his arms and legs about would cause the bystanders to laugh, whereas a regiment of men doing the same thing in unison is a matter for pride—or fear—in the onlookers. Being used to the sight of one's own soldiers has a good deal to do with one's reactions. The British thrill with patriotic fervour at the sight of a guardsman raising his knees to the level of his waist and stamping iron-shod boots in the forecourt of Buckingham Palace. To an American, accustomed to troops in rubber-soled shoes, this is funny. The Englishman in his turn considers the German soldier, who raises not only his knees but the whole length of his lower leg as well for *his* ceremonial march, comic, while all three look upon the quick pace of the French as something quite excruciating.

There are two serious points in all this. The first is that the system of discipline and constant repetition, the insistence that the soldier is supposed not to think but only to obey, is all too effective in its purpose, which is to change an uncertain, unpredictable human being into a machine. The second point is that the soldiers subjected to their formal drill, the officers who elaborate the drill and make the soldiers do it, and the spectators alike all tend to allow their minds to become dulled and to forget what the original purpose was that the stamping and shouting and marching up and down were intended to achieve. The industrialisation of civilian society leads to the rigidities that we have been discussing. Military discipline has always involved submission to an ever more demanding and fixed system of behaviour. And now that war too has become industrialised, quite remarkable stresses have developed.

The framework of civilian rigidity was originally constructed so that the nation submitting to it could enjoy the wealth and comfort, the ample supplies of varied foods—frozen, canned, dehydrated and brightly coloured—the freedom from disease, and the facility for travel and pleasure that applied science can bring. If in time the people began to forget why they were submitting themselves to the hardship and drudgery of dull hours in factories, ugly houses, smoky air and the incessant drumbeat of admonition that to stop work and enjoy the scent of roses on a weekday was sin—if this came about, it was a gradual process. It could be said as well that they had only themselves to blame. But for men in an army at war things are different. The system is set up for them, and the forgetfulness of the generals in charge of it falls on the heads of the soldiers.

It would be unfair to blame generals for their forgetfulness, which is no greater than that of the rest of the population, did it not have such an unfortunate effect on so large a number of other people. The history of pre-scientific generals is full of examples of disasters that, it seems, might have been avoided by a little thoughtfulness and the memory of what had happened before. But the most fundamental lesson is to avoid a rigid adherence to a system just because it exists, when the circumstances that made it useful have changed. This is often rudely called the 'military mind'. A 'military bearing' is the outward and visible sign that the regimental machinery—or, in plain language, the system of practice and drill and practice again that comprises military training—has done its work. It leaves a recognisable mark on a man, as it is intended to do, and this is good. But the 'military mind', used in a pejorative sense, is a symptom that the machinery has had a crippling effect.

'... *disasters that might have been avoided* ...'

The Science Myth

The battle of Crécy, fought 600 odd years ago in 1346, demonstrated quite clearly that it was unwise for men to advance, either mounted or on foot, in the face of a discharge of accurate missile fire. To put it bluntly, the French knights found that they were unable to charge when opposed by well-aimed volleys from the English longbowmen. Almost 550 years later, in December 1899, the same circumstances arose again at Colenso. This was one of several important battles of the Boer War in South Africa each of which demonstrated the same thing. This time it was not accurate archery from longbowmen at 200 yards but accurate rifle fire from Mausers at 700 yards. And this time it was not French knights and English bowmen but British professional troops and amateur Boer riflemen. The principle, however, was identical. The lesson was the same. The moral is that regimental machinery demanding rigid conformity for its own sake will, in the long run, be painful to endure. Here is Colenso:

> At an early stage of the action Long's guns whirled forwards, outstripped the infantry brigades upon their flanks, . . . and unlimbered within seven hundred—some say five hundred—yards of the enemy trenches. From this position he opened fire upon Fort Wylie, which was the centre of that portion of the Boer position which faced him. But his two unhappy batteries were not destined to turn the tide of battle as he had hoped, but rather to furnish the classic example of the helplessness of artillery against modern rifle fire. Not even Mercer's famous description of the effect of flank fire upon his troop of horse artillery at Waterloo could do justice to the blizzard of lead which broke over the two doomed batteries. The teams fell in heaps, some dead, some mutilated, and mutilating others in their frantic struggles. . . . But a perfect discipline reigned amid the vast majority of the gunners, and the words of command and the laying and working of the guns were as methodical as at Okehampton. . . . Already every gun had its litter of dead around it, but

each was still fringed by its own group of furious officers and sweating, desperate gunners. . . . Officers and men were falling fast. The guns could not be worked, and yet they could not be removed, for every effort to bring up teams from the shelter where the limbers lay ended in the death of the horses.*

This is a tragic description of the strong endeavours of men disciplined by a rigid system possessing many admirable qualities. In its different context the system of discipline exacted of scientific technology is equally admirable. It is not for nothing that the chairman presents a gold watch to the long-service operative who has spent a lifetime bending over his machine—laying and firing at the word of command, cheerfully with no murmur of complaint—in the plastic drain-pipe factory. The peculiar tragedy of the loss of the guns at Colenso and of the men and horses was that it could have been avoided by *thinking*. The musketry at the Battle of Waterloo in 1815, eighty-five years before, was not of a very high standard, yet it had taken toll of horse artillery then. And the precision of gun-fire was still being improved in 1854 when the charge of the Light Brigade took place in the Crimean War. Both these events demonstrated that men could not gallop about on battlefields in the face of the technological developments then occurring. Chemical advances in the composition of propellents; engineering advances in the construction of weapons; invention, calculation and thought in the design of rifling to improve the accuracy of the flight of bullets—all these steps in scientific and technological progress were occurring, and were known to be occurring. Yet the system was in existence; the regimental machinery was a rigid and respected contrivance and the soldiers must conform to it. The purpose of the red coats and the cavalry swords and lances, the drill demanding that the guns should be all in a line, wheel to wheel and in the open, the reason why the men had been taught not

* From *The Great Boer War*, by Sir Arthur Conan Doyle. (Nelson.)

to think—'their's not to reason why, their's but to do and die',
as Tennyson put it—had been forgotten.

The Boers in South Africa in 1899 were amateurs. They
possessed no regimental machinery to cherish and keep
polished. They had no rigid traditional system to which they
were expected to conform. They did their fighting in frock-
coats and beards and this allowed them to behave according to
their native wit. Sir Arthur Conan Doyle remarked at the time:

> The very great advantage which the Boers possessed—one
> which enabled half a dozen Boer guns to hold as many
> British batteries—was that their cannon were as invisible as
> their rifles. The first use which a Boer makes of his guns is to
> conceal them. The first use which a British major makes of
> his is to expose them in a straight line with correct inter-
> spaces, each gun so near its neighbour that a lucky shell
> dropping between them might cripple the crews of each.
> The artillery are a highly educated scientific corps, so the
> outsider must conclude that there is some deep reason for
> this arrangement; but whatever this reason may be, it most
> certainly does not apply to a war like this.

There have been many well-run societies and there have
been well-run armies too. The danger arises when big changes
take place. When this happens a system designed for a particular purpose needs to be changed to meet the changed circumstances. If the system has become rigid, however, and
people are not willing to change it then it begins to impose itself on them. It is interesting to note that the Lateran council
passed a decree in 1139 banning the crossbow as an undesirable
and deadly weapon not to be tolerated in the system of war
then operated by properly brought-up generals. This reluctance to abandon a fixed routine of behaviour—be it the belief
that the breadwinner of a two-car family ought to go on working in a factory just as diligently as an underfed Congolese, or
that a cavalry charge is a good way to capture a machine-gun
post—leads to particularly severe results in our own times

when science and technology are changing conditions at the rate they are.

In 1900, the historian of the Boer War commenting on the new and destructive effect of precision Mauser rifle-fire prophesied that in the future 'some portable bullet-proof shield would be invented'. Forty years and two major wars later science and technology achieved this end by the really serious development of tanks.

The object of a modern tank is to enable a soldier to perform destructive military activities in reasonable comfort and safety. Gibbon put it rather neatly when he wrote, in another context, that they 'tend to improve (if such improvement can be wished) the art of destroying the human species'. However, almost the whole of the technical advantage of tanks can be lost if the engineers who make them overlook the fact that their comparative indestructibility and their fire-power will be of no avail if they are too rigidly constructed for men to ride in them comfortably. And the generals also will fail to benefit even from a perfect engineering design if when ordering tanks into battle they forget that they are really giving a command to armoured men.

In World War II, the United States Army applied the last word in science to the development of a particular type of tank. It could move about with unequalled speed, its gun could reach long distances and the shells it fired could penetrate the skin of other tanks no matter how thick they might be. Alternatively, if there were no other tanks to destroy it could kill people, quickly, expeditiously, without fuss and in large numbers. Inside, it was filled with telephones and range-finders and other technical devices to control it in action and keep it in touch with the other tanks in its squadron. When this unexampled product of scientific and technological skill was tried out in practice it was found that its performance was not always as good as had been anticipated. When the matter was investigated it was found that some tank commanders were getting themselves killed through not shutting the lid. Worse still, it was found that it was sometimes not possible to shut the lid. This was because although there was a distance of 3 feet 6 inches between the seat inside the tank and the bottom of the lid when it was shut, the sitting height of the biggest men who had to manage the tank was 3 feet 6½ inches with their helmets on. Rarely can there have been a more vivid instance of the principles of Procrustes in action. If the lid was properly shut, the tall tank commanders were literally crushed into their iron cases; and if they left the lid open they had the tops of their heads shot off!

Ergonomics is becoming a detailed and complex scientific study and even in 1942 and 1943 the human engineers at Fort Knox, Kentucky, went into the problem of fitting tanks to men with great thoroughness. In the olden days, the members of armoured corps had their armour made to measure. In these modern days of mass production this is not possible, but it is possible to determine the measurements of the 'average soldier', just as Stephen Leacock once assessed the characteristics of the 'average Englishwoman'. All sorts of measurements were made of large numbers of men; besides their height, the human engineers recorded their reach at full stretch sideways and forwards, their width with arms akimbo, the length of their forearms, the depth and breadth of their chests, the width of their hips, the distance from their buttocks to their knees when they were sitting down—some of the makers of mini-cars could usefully turn up this record—the height of their knee-caps above the floor, the length of their feet, the distance from their eyes to the tops of their heads, and the extent of their hand's breadth.

In any lifetime it seems to be the melancholy truth that we can expect that something of the order of a tenth will be lived—assuming we survive—with our society at war. Wartime is, it seems, merely an accentuation of peacetime. And since we live in peace as in war in a machine environment, it is interesting to notice that when the Fort Knox scientists began to take a serious, scientific interest in the average human bottom and the design of the seats installed in tanks they discovered a remarkable number of ways in which men were forced to conform to the structure of the seats rather than *vice versa*. For example, the numerous measurements made of the sizes and shapes of the men when referred to the measurements of the seats showed quite clearly that large numbers of tank drivers and their assistants could not get their eyes properly in line with the periscope of the tank which was installed to show them where they were going. Either it was not possible to raise the seat high enough, or else, when the seat was raised, the distance from the top of their helmets to the centre of their eyeballs was more than the structure of the tank could contain.

In a technological age, it is difficult for a human individual to maintain his rights. Civilians hardly like to complain that table legs are in their way, that cupboard doors open the wrong way, or that the upholstered motorcar of the current year's vintage gives one a pain in the back if it is driven for more than two hours at a time. The direct application of ergonometric studies to the seats of the tanks showed, however, exactly where the regimental machinery was pinching. Not only were there large numbers of tank commanders and gun loaders whose stature was such that they were not able to use the seats efficiently at all as things to be sat on, but for the man who could sit down, the seats wobbled, vibrated and sometimes broke and those in the tank turrets interfered with the circulation of the sitters' legs.

And so it was that the orginal engineering design of World War II tanks had to be modified to meet the needs of the bodies and heads and limbs they were to contain. But besides this, they also had to be modified to allow the men in them to breathe. It was only after some considerable measure of suffering that it was found that when the gun in the tank was let off, the concentration of carbon monoxide inside the vehicle rose so high that the crew were in imminent danger of being poisoned. And even if they were not overcome by carbon monoxide, the amount of ammonia produced by the explosion was enough to blind the gunner and the commander, while the loader, in the position in which he was sitting, suffered a higher concentration still until the tears streamed from his eyes and he was gasping for breath. Nevertheless, it can on the other hand be noted that a study of the effect of the noise produced when the tank was moving about the battlefield firing its gun showed that the men inside were not permanently deafened but only suffered from a 'transient ringing in the ears'.

War, being as it were an accentuation of peace, shows in an exaggerated form the stresses in society caused by scientific technology. The new developments come more quickly to meet the tensions of the situation; their purpose seems clearer than the purpose of similar progress in peacetime. In war, the purpose is for our side to succeed and to destroy the enemy so that then—and here ideas become rather hazy—we can be prosperous and live happily ever after. In peace, though the battle may sometimes be as severe, the goal does not appear in such sharp focus. One can, of course, set up a five-year plan at the end of which the Promised Land will be reached, but in general the aim moves mistily away for ever. In war, we can justify rigidities in the name of discipline, without which battles cannot be won. And should a number of people be crippled or killed by the pulling and pushing of the regimental machinery, well, there is the urgency of using the new science to win the war as soon as possible.

In June 1915 the British Army decided to adopt the scientific principle of using the poison gas, chlorine, as a weapon of war. The development of this new technological process was telescoped by the exigencies of the times, so that the problems, administrative, disciplinary and technical, of using so novel an idea became quite dramatically accentuated. Today, the appropriate use of scientifically trained men in civilian life is a constant preoccupation. In 1915, the same problem was considered, a decision reached, and an order issued that chemistry teachers, students and qualified chemists alike should be taken from any part of the army where they might be found and gathered together into a Special Brigade. Each man, regardless of his relative scientific status, was given the rank of corporal and the duty of carrying chlorine cylinders about, connecting and disconnecting gas pipes and turning valves on and off. This was the authority of the times: that scientific manpower should be so used. Today in our civilian life we have a 'war winning' aim as well and the rigidities of the times—not so severe as those of 1915, but powerful nevertheless—decree that scientific manpower shall be concentrated to increase the economic and material strength of the nation.

The first British gas attack at Loos on 25 September 1915 was not a particularly outstanding success of applied scientific effort. The chemical corporals had been trained to carry gas cylinders along trenches and were acquainted with the operation of the protective respirators designed to prevent them from choking themselves rather than their opponents. They were transported to the battlefield in London buses especially mobilised for the occasion, and the fighting soldiers who were to capture the territory after the chlorine had fulfilled its purpose were assembled. But then arose the troublesome difficulties which prudent industrialists expect whenever a new process is to be commissioned. The gas pipes for distributing the chlorine with which the men had been so diligently drilled during their training were too long and could not be got round the corners of the front-line trenches. The pipes were connected in sections and the sections connected to the gas cylinders by screw joints which under the exigencies of practical operations were found to leak chlorine on to the men who were attempting to handle them. The cylinders themselves had been exposed to rain and mud during their laborious journey to the scene of operations, and on many of them the taps had become corroded so that they could not be turned on. And when the order came at last, 'Turn on the gas!' it was found that when those of the cylinders that could be opened were opened full on, the chlorine came out as a liquid and not a gas at all.

Here in microcosm was a military example of devotion to technological aims showing in an accentuated and dramatised form the virtues that it brings out of the men subjected to it as well as the harm it does. The main virtues were loyalty and discipline supported by courage. The gas corporals had been trained in their duties, their wills had been bent to conform. As qualified chemists they may have doubted the success of the operation in view of the equipment at their disposal, the difficulties of operating it in a muddy battlefield under enemy fire and the state of the wind when the 'off' was given; nevertheless, their training and loyalty kept them true to their duty when the time came. In civilian life, there are other men to be found devoting their energies in factories and refineries to apparatus and equipment that they know full well could be improved, and manufacturing products ranging from gin and chlorophyll toothpaste all the way to hydrogen bombs and inter-continental ballistic missiles, in whose ultimate usefulness for the increase in human happiness and prosperity they may feel private doubts. Nevertheless, at Loos the chemists were prepared to choke themselves and burn themselves and get themselves blown up because they had dedicated themselves so to do.

The technological framework of the use of gas in warfare soon showed itself to be readily capable of modification and development into a successful example of applied science. By October, an efficient system for turning the gas cylinders on and off had been worked out, short pipes had been substituted for the inconvenient long ones, flexible rubber connections were installed in place of the unsatisfactory and leaky screw connections, and atomisers were fixed on to the ends of the pipes so that the chlorine would come out as a gas and not in the form of a dangerous and ineffective liquid spray. It is reported that at the attack on Hulloch Redoubt on 13 October 1915 the operation was a 'marked success'. That is to say, German soldiers at the receiving end were effectively poisoned by chlorine rather than the British soldiers at the delivery end.

Nevertheless, it is difficult to assert that either for the limited military objective of exterminating troops in an opposing army in war or for the more extended aim of achieving the higher happiness of man, the proceeding as a whole had been really worth while. The specifications of this particular piece of regimental machinery, to which the communities of soldiers on both sides of World War I willingly submitted themselves, demanded first that they put their minds to devising an application of chemical science by which men in opposing forces could be poisoned. The killing of enemies in war is a habit to which mankind has so long and so readily conformed that it can hardly be claimed that it is one of the peculiar customs deriving from the Procrustean system. Nevertheless, no matter how clear-headed and logical we may be about the necessity of the particular war in which we happen to be involved, and the palpable rightness of our side compared with the obvious turpitude of the other side—in spite of all this, even the most insensitive of us must feel a twinge at having to be trained to do what it is we are about to undertake.

But perhaps a more valid criticism of the work and effort of the chemists who chose and made the gas—first chlorine, then phosgene, then more esoteric compounds like Mustard Gas and Lewisite; and of the technologists who elaborated the hardware by which they were to be delivered; of the officers who worked out the training systems by which effective and efficient gas warfare was to be waged; and of the soldiers who immolated themselves in the learning and drilling and doing of all the things that had to be done, was that they failed in their purpose. After having achieved the whole elaborate proceeding of supplying the gas and its cylinders, and its delivery to the battle-line, and having drilled and trained and instructed everybody in the entire operation, it didn't work. The upshot was that the soldiers, already equipped with every modern technological device of warfare—entrenching tools, catering equipment, bandages, water-purification tablets, armoured helmets, binoculars and iron rations—found themselves (in both armies)—burdened with one thing more: an anti-gas respirator.

It is a natural instinct in peace as well as in war to compress

49

ourselves more than we need into the burdensome conformity of a modern community, by carrying about bulky objects as protection against possible pains and dangers—which only threaten us because of the things we ourselves do and, more often than not, do not in the end happen. From the manager in his boardroom, worrying about life insurance, to the middle-aged operative in the workshop, eager for as much overtime as he can get to add to the protection against the rainy day that may never come, much of life in a modern technological community is hampered by such impedimenta, as protection against the troubles we fear when our days of 'employment' are over.

The military training that in all its ramifications forms the rigid framework about which I have been writing can be painful and can do great harm. In some respects, however, the rigid conformity by which we are bent, it may be permanently, can bring progress and advancement because of the drastic nature of war itself. The condensed description of some of the military incidents of the reign of King Hezekiah have often attracted attention. It will be remembered that the King of Assyria, after a successful campaign and the payment of substantial reparations by Hezekiah—namely, three hundred talents of silver and thirty talents of gold—mounted a major offensive against Jerusalem. So sure was he of success that he accompanied this by a propaganda barrage that, even allowing for the brutality of the times, was of a particularly offensive nature. However, he overlooked one important factor in military discipline, sanitation. The writer of II Kings, 19, described the event in these words: 'And it came to pass that night, that the angel of the Lord went out, and smote in the camp of the Assyrians an hundred fourscore and five thousand; and when they arose early in the morning, behold, they were all dead corpses. So Sennacherib king of Assyria departed, and went and returned, and dwelt at Nineveh.' Or, as Byron put it:

And the might of the Gentile, unsmote by the sword,
Hath melted like snow in the glance of the Lord!

War, Forgetfulness and the Human Bottom

It is perhaps unfair to blame Sennacherib or his three generals, Tartan, Rabsaris and Rabshakeh, for allowing the medical services of their forces to become slack. They may not have known any better. It has been pointed out by Zinsser, however, in his book published in 1935 that to the average professional officer, the military doctor is an unwillingly tolerated noncombatant who looks after sick parades, issues cathartic pills, makes transportation troubles, complicates tactical plans, and chlorinates the drinking water. Nevertheless, the lesson preached by Zinsser has now been accepted by intelligent soldiers. It is that of all the painful mutilations of their military machine the most lethal is disease. By confining armies of men within the rigidities of a military force, epidemic diseases of all sorts—spread by water, lice, rats, fleas or famine—kill and disable more destructively than the enemy.

Xerxes lost 300,000 out of 800,000 of his men from disease in his war against Greece. Between 1098 and 1099 the Christian army besieging Antioch dwindled from 300,000 men to 60,000; the rest died of disease and so did 5000 of their 7000 horses. And of the residual 60,000 victorious over the heathen, only one in three survived to the year 1101. But we need not go back to the pre-scientific history of armies for examples of the sort of things that had afflicted the Assyrians. In the Crimean War, of all others the most agonising example of what happens when people plunge themselves into a system—a rigidly organised military society—without taking some thought as to how to avoid the worst results of such rigidity, there was already some knowledge of what could be done. Miss Nightingale and her devoted ladies showed this as soon as they had the chance. And yet cholera, typhus and dysentery cut down the men just as if it had still been a biblical war.

Yet it is to some of the extreme rigours of the discipline of war that we owe important and lasting benefits. The public appreciation of the medical and sanitary disasters of the Crimean War which were brought to general notice by the vigour of Miss Nightingale and her loftily placed relations and supporters taught a lesson that was never completely forgotten. There have been army commanders since her time who have ignored the principles of military medicine and hygiene. These have sometimes been men who have thought it soldierly virtue to suffer whatever may come on the battlefield—even if it might be preventable. But it is generally accepted nowadays that commanders cannot allow themselves the luxury of the amateur enjoyment of forlorn hopes and gallant deaths, that inevitably involve their men as well as themselves, if they can be avoided and the same ends achieved by more informed methods.

The system of army medical services that Miss Nightingale developed from her experiences at Scutari have been a permanent gain, not only to the men involved in armies at war but to civilised communities in general. So has her organisation of the training of nurses, and the Army Medical College which she virtually founded. The pressures and tensions of wars since the Crimea have accelerated the search for ways to avoid medical disasters. In World War II, the medical services of the armies made immense efforts to find ways to keep soldiers fit and free from harm—as prison doctors tend the welfare of men condemned to hang. And much of the solid research and ingenious innovation to provide ration scales of appropriate foods; uniform clothing for warmth, comfort, protection and concealment; disease-free environments under difficult and discouraging conditions; and a systematic and intelligible categorisation of wounds and diseases so that these could be put right with the minimum of administrative fuss—much of this was of permanent value.

The application of science to war, even when it produced strains and stresses for the men who had to use it in battles, has often benefited people in their ordinary lives afterwards. World War I led to substantial advances in science applied to aviation. At the time, the pilots and crews suffered discomfort, hardship and sometimes death. The people down below suffered too, but the technical progress made soon enabled them to enjoy the pleasures of rapid travel all over the world and, until this itself set into the rigid framework of a new kind of technological living, as we shall discuss in Chapter 8, there were new avenues for happiness and interest. In World War II, the aviation germinated in World War I acquired the further benefit of radar invented to meet the military exigencies of plotting the movements of attacking battleships and bombers.

And now, latest of all, we have the application of fundamental physical theory to give an efficiency undreamed of by Gibbon to the ancient military operation of exterminating humanity. Atomic physics is an intellectual exercise so theoretical as hardly to exist in the material world at all. The solid rocks, the lumps of uranium heavier than lead, are composed, so theorise the physicists, of particles so small that they cannot be seen; not only can they not be seen but it is theoretically impossible to see *one* because, says Heisenberg, the light by which it might be seen would itself knock it off course. And yet out of this abstruse and harmless mathematics came an engine of war for which great Caesars would have given cartloads of gold. Now we are to gain from it atomic power for warmth and comfort and to run the trains.

And from the pestilence of war, often the worst mutilation of military immobility, we were left, when the soldiers stopped fighting, with penicillin, which their urgent need for relief had brought. Penicillin was known to exist when World War II began—it had been discovered by Fleming in 1929—but at that time no one could make it in quantity. It was not until the war of 1939 began to exert its strains on the community that extraordinary efforts were made to manufacture penicillin to mitigate the worst distress of the disease and wounds inevitably accompanying such a war. The discovery of penicillin had been a first-class stroke of original thinking and experiment, the discovery of ways of manufacturing it in bulk was a development in technological practice of almost equal orginality. Up till then, the traditional way to handle micro-organisms was in small individual culture flasks. The first attempt at multiplying the amount of penicillin produced by its particular strain of mould was to multiply the number of flasks. One of the first innovations to circumvent the shortages of war was the use of milk bottles instead of special flasks. These were used in enormous numbers. And then under the stress of war, the intellectual leap was taken and 'biochemical engineering', as it is often called now, was invented. From this we benefit today in peace.

The rigid framework of the self-imposed discipline of a scientific community at war can be dreadfully wrong, or it can be splendidly right. It is dreadfully wrong when a system designed for one purpose is allowed to continue when circumstances have changed.

The regimental machinery elaborated to deal with the demands of modern war in the present technological age is a particularly cramping thing because it is so extensive. Its discomforts extend from dreadful mutilations from incendiary bombing all the way to such trivial trials as the frustrations of the black-out. A particularly disagreeable feature is its pervasiveness when fought in the modern uncivilised manner of 'the nation at war'. This is a comparatively new arrangement when considered in historical terms and is very largely due to the application of technology to fighting. This not only enables combatants to cover a large area with their fast-flying aeroplanes and their long-range missiles but it also requires the use of a substantial proportion of the national industry for the manufacture of war machines. And one of the most serious human pressures arising from the rigidity of the rigours of war is the social disruption it causes with a whole nation in arms, instead of merely the warring of two professional armies.

Biological science has demonstrated, so far as present knowledge is available, that the notion that genetically one nation is 'better' than another is a fallacy and the hypothesis that one nation is born to rule and another to obey is untenable. Rather it is more rational to consider, in any particular war in which one may find oneself engaged, that the enemy of the moment is an ally who, on this occasion, happens to be on the wrong side. This was perhaps forgotten by the World War II generals who maintained one of the most hurtful of the rigidities of war by forbidding their troops from 'fraternising' when, clearly, the most effective and agreeable of the methods for repairing the disharmonies of war is to settle down and marry one's enemy.

4

WE'VE GOT IT ON
THE BRAIN

THE MINDS of the Scots have resisted the squeezing of the
modern pressures towards uniformity better than those of the
English. This is demonstrated by the difference between the
English and the Scottish catechisms. The English catechism
begins in a matter-of-fact businesslike way by asking: 'What
is your name?'; the Scottish: 'What is the chief end of man?'

In the present-day world, it is natural to think that scientific
progress is the obvious and inevitable process of events. When
the horse was the fastest means of locomotion, and always had
been, it was reasonable to think that this was decreed by fate:
so fast and no faster. And we can assume that this way of
thinking was fully compatible with happiness. Alternatively,
there were large numbers of people who never bothered at all
about the speed of horses. Things are different now, however.
Somehow or other the pressure increased so that a hundred
years ago in the nineteenth century it became overwhelmingly
strong. 'Technological progress is good' was the motto, and
'technological progress is inevitable and will continue for ever.
Everybody says so.' And because this is what everbody
thought, the pressure became so powerful that no mind could
resist its influence.

And the second thing that 'everybody' knows is that science
can achieve anything. The implication of every government
pronouncement, of every business statement, of newspaper
articles, and the forecasts of five-year plans is that this is so.
And at last the mind becomes convinced that it is true. Can we
not fly? Can we not see things that are happening on the other
side of the world? Why should we not think that science will
prevent our catching cold? And when colds are brought to an

end, the next ill to be dealt with will be cancer or coronary heart disease. We think this today; why should our children not think next that science can stop *all* diseases and then we can live for ever!

First of all, however, is the assumption with which nobody quarrels—that is nobody who is dedicated to a life of industrial work (for five days a week of course, with week-ends and evenings for 'real' life)—that the object of society is to increase productivity and exports, harden the currency, and increase the gold and dollar reserves. In order that adults shall satisfactorily fit into this framework of ideas, their minds must be moulded from childhood onwards to accept the correctness of the premise upon which the whole system is based.

To a child, his father and mother are at first wonderful and to be admired. He would like to grow up to be like them. The little ignorant creature cannot see that his father is tied down to his five-day week (plus overtime, of course) manufacturing refrigerators and that his mother once operated a comptometer. The parents are inured to the system and raise no objection to their offspring being set on the path to an education specifically designed to fit them for employment in industry when their turn comes. The pupils must be encouraged to bend their minds to the task of winning a General Certificate of Education—so that they will qualify for a good job. Industrialists complain that candidates for employment cannot write clear reports or satisfactory business letters. The school syllabus must therefore be adjusted to include sufficient lessons in English appropriately planned, not to instil a love of letters or the enjoyment of the riches of literature and an acquaintance with the great men and women of the past, but to influence the minds of the children so that, when they are grown up, they may be capable of preparing a succinct report —on one sheet of foolscap—for the chairman of the board of directors. For those children whose minds possess the facility for languages there must be instruction in French and German and perhaps Russian as well and they must be impressed with the importance of this knowledge for the increase in international trade and, above all, to enable them to read scientific and technical reports.

More than this is required, however. Before they leave school and relinquish their childhood years their minds must already be well stocked with science and technology. Science must be taught, not as an intellectual discipline, not as an example of how the mind of man has been enabled to grasp in its compass the secrets of nature and an understanding of the working of the universe, but as a training to fit them for the 9 to 5 world of the factory in which they are destined to spend that portion of their day that the industrial system demands before they can use the rest for real living. Industrial nations expect to receive a portion of young people's time and energy while they are still at school as if they were already in a factory. Their minds, in fact, are being formed for the part of living which most of them later on will feel that they have to sacrifice to what they would rather not be doing.

A few people have already noticed the way in which the present age brings pressure on the minds of the young. Professor D. W. Harding has appealed to those who guide society in Britain and its Commonwealth to relinquish the use of education as a preparation of children for industry. He recognises that if the British want to continue the pursuit of material wealth that they have been keeping up so vigorously for the last two centuries, they must be prepared to accept the consequences. Yet he calls still for education to be a training of the mind for the good life. And Dr Lloyd Davies, Chief Medical Officer of the Ministry of Labour in London, has gone on record as demanding that young workers at least, whose technical training is part of their daily employment, should be freed in working hours to be taught also about men and manners and what has been thought and done by great men so that their minds, bent as they are towards technology, may be bent back and so made straighter.

There have been so many examples in history of peoples

suffering sorrows and pains that they inflict upon themselves, that we who live right at the end of all this history ought not to be surprised any more. What then can be more natural than to find that it is the very parents who have themselves been mutilated in conforming to the demands of industrial civilisation who are most insistent that the minds of their children should be similarly confined. More and more British children are staying on into the sixth form at school. Some of them may receive a full and rounded education during the two precious years when their minds, physiologically and anatomically mature as thinking engines, are as yet empty of knowledge. They are the few who may be able to resist the cramping attack of the technological system they will meet in later life. For the majority of children, the school course to which they are exposed at the age of 15 or 16 in the sixth forms, where the cream of the younger generation once used to obtain the foundation of a real higher education, is simply a specialist cramming period. And it is the parents who demand that the curriculum should be arranged in this way, so that they can be assured that their children will be well prepared for the factory, the workshop and the laboratory. The younger children learn to read and look about them, and when they are, say, 14 years old forty per cent of their teaching will deal with science and numbers and sixty per cent with the diverse other matters of the various world they live in. Then, when they reach 16, if they are bright and their parents ambitious, two-thirds of the school time is devoted to mathematics and science. Only one-third of their time for learning is left for non-'useful' subjects (including physical training), the learning of English, the doings of people past and present and thoughts of grace or beauty.

In case it should be thought that it is necessary for the minds of people in the modern world to be moulded solely to the requirements of the material society in which we like to live and that it is inevitable that the 'prison bars that close around the growing boy'—as Wordsworth put it—should be an exclusive and wholehearted devotion to technology, look for a moment at the Indians. Here it has been found possible for two kinds of people to live together: those who have sacrificed themselves to the exigencies of 'productivity', and those others who, while poor, superstitious and fatalistic, make the dominating features of their lives religion and the family. It seems possible for the former to co-operate with the latter and use science and technology on their behalf without making it a dominating influence. The educated victims of scientific materialism, for their part, may be able too to enjoy some of the freedom of mind of the ignorant but intelligent villagers. For example, Professor Leslie Banks, when he attended the great religious fair of Ardh Kumbh in Allahabad, was housed in a magnificent tent fit for Akbar himself. Here his mind could be free from material preoccupations except for the fact that the tent was wired for electric light and sacred music relayed by loudspeaker.

The great population of India, whose minds are untouched by the influence of technology, gather every sixth year in millions to bathe at the confluence of the sacred rivers Ganges, Jumna and Saraswati. This, they think, is a meritorious thing to do. Before the days of science, these religious festivals were the source of the great epidemics of cholera. Even in 1948 a severe outbreak of cholera followed the Ardh Kumbh. In 1954 several hundred people were crushed to death but, for the first time, compulsory cholera inoculation was enforced. That is to say, the minds of the people could think what they pleased. The ideas bringing them to the river to be purified—five million came on the main bathing day of 1948—had no relation with technology. Their presence was unconnected with the gold and dollar reserves or the export drive. Yet it seems they were prepared to use scientific methods to achieve their quite unscientific ends.

For the 1960 Ardh Kumbh festival the devotees of scientific technology collaborated with magnificent success with the devotees of religion. When the pilgrims arrived they made their way early in the morning to their family priest, the pragwal, where he sat on the banks of the Ganges with his distinguishing flag flying over his head. Then they went off to submit themselves to ceremonial shaving as the first part of their purification. For this purification to be effective their cut hair must be cast into the holy river. At this point, the scientific health authorities stepped in and collected the hair from them, packed it into gunny bags and consigned it to the sacred waters, but did so by taking it off in a boat and disposing of it in a deep part of the river.

When purified by shaving, the pilgrim returned to his pragwal who led his disciples to bathe. Professor Banks has given a vivid description of the event, of the camp area by the river of thirty-five square miles where there are houses for the well-to-do, huts along the water-side for the less well off, and a sandy plain for the great multitude of the people who live and sleep in the open during at least five days of religious exercises. He describes how on the main bathing day—not of biblical times but of the recent year of 1960 in this present technological era—four million pilgrims came by rail, by river and by road, by bus, double-decker bullock cart, bicycle, tonga or on foot.

But when this devout crowd approached the sacred stream they were confronted at every point by a circle of twenty inoculation barriers where all those unable to produce a certificate of recent inoculation were immunised against cholera. At this stage it was the scientific thinkers who had to defer, at least in some degree, to those whose thoughts were of religion. As Professor Banks describes it: 'Any delay was liable to cause resentment and the (medical) staffs had to work at high speed and with great tact.'

But the scientific technologists did a splendid job. For example, they divided up the whole area of the river bank into seven circles, each under the control of a medical officer. These officers organised an elaborate system of trench latrines which were systematically sprinkled with lime and filled in as occasion demanded. Absentminded pilgrims who failed to take advantage of them were tactfully impelled to do so by sanitary officers who were on duty from four o'clock each morning. Rubbish and garbage were collected and scientifically disposed of. Flies were exterminated by every modern means, and water was brought in from the city and tested regularly for bacteriological purity. Even the sacred waters of the Ganges, the Jumna and the Saraswati were examined for microbiological and chemical purity, although their powers of spiritual purification were accepted as an article of faith by the millions who were drawn to their banks and for whom the skill and devotion of the medical teams—inhabitants, it would seem, almost of another world—were so selflessly and effectively deployed.

But although this remarkable example of the combination of people whose minds have been influenced by the impact of modern science and technology and those others whose intellects still remain moved by other forces—tradition, devotion to a religious faith, perhaps superstition—seems like a happy and mutually advantageous combination, yet the great crowd whose thinking is as yet uninfluenced by the strong power of technology cannot stay so indefinitely. The very freedom from disaster, from cholera, dysentery, disorder and death which the men of the New Technology have given them must itself make them change. Perhaps the most poignant passage in Professor Banks's account of the great festival of the 1960 Ardh Kumbh on the banks of the Ganges is his description of the side-shows. After their religious duties are done the pilgrims can visit the booths of the sweetmeat sellers and conjurers set up for their enjoyment. But now, most prominent of all among these was the large pavilion erected by the health authorities to popularise birth-control.

'Situated centrally, and picked out in coloured and moving electric lights at night, it was visible from a great distance and attracted many thousands of visitors,' wrote Professor Banks. And when they came they were able to walk round, listen to the demonstrators, examine the exhibits and, if they wished, go into the separate compartments for men and women to receive

technical instructions. Here, vividly dramatised, is the meeting point of two paths. Those who advance towards scientific technology can command wealth and power and control over their environment. These things are within their grasp if they think what they are doing—if they have the wit to remain free from the rigid pursuit of hollow materialism that has already claimed whole nations as victims. Science gives power over disease and, when it is used, the death-rate falls and populations increase. It is reasonable, therefore, that the use of science to keep alive the Ganges pilgrims who would otherwise die of the cholera should be accompanied by a parallel use of science to check the uncontrolled flow of new life. By this means the people can worship in safety. But science and technology lead to manufacture and industry and, if the minds of a community come to worship productivity and the scientific way as divinities, dishwashers, deep-freeze cabinets and air-conditioners become as embarrassingly numerous as babies. Then the question is not whether to refrain from another child in order to be able safely to make a pilgrimage, but whether to have a second car rather than a second child.

The pre-1960 pilgrims on the banks of the Ganges were confined by disease and poverty. Their problem now is how, while taking the path of scientific technology, at the same time to use the richer life it will bring to good advantage.

It is to the glory of mankind that the taking of a wife is a matter to call forth devotion, love and joy. And these high qualities can develop to the full when science has lifted the grinding burdens of poverty, hardship and disease. Living as he did in a pre-scientific age, Romeo was fortunate that the Montague family to which he belonged was comparatively well to do. His mind fixed on Juliet gave us, in words put into his mouth by Shakespeare, a high example of idealism, beauty and sacrifice:

With love's light wings did I o'er-perch these walls:
For stony limits cannot hold love out.

There are good reasons why it is prudent for both partners to submit to a psychological examination before engaging themselves to marry, and the ruling that a thorough clinical examination together with a blood test should be made before the young people legally consummate their love is surely a wise arrangement. But this is a point where some of the more warm-hearted members of modern industrial communities feel that the system under which we have chosen to live is pressing on them too intrusively. These, though their minds are moulded to accept the need for tests and examinations, may feel at least a pang at giving up a fiancée when her blood test shows that she is incompatible.

The member of an advanced nation is impelled not only to devote the set part of each twenty-four hours to his factory duties for the whole middle period of his life, but he should also choose his wife and organise his family to suit the industrial process too. A successful technology requires the existence of very large business units—it is immaterial whether their senior executives owe allegiance to shareholders or the State. And the right men to run these concerns must have the right kind of wives. This means far more than the right race, the appropriate genetical and psychological make-up and freedom from an agreed list of hereditary or acquired diseases. Packard has recently pointed out that the larger and more advanced industrial corporations in the United States insist that officials who are engaged to run them are selected, not only for their technical and administrative abilities, but also on their possession of a suitable wife—suitable, that is to say, for the purpose of the corporation. The minds of the people who manage a large corporation are fixed on the need for their company to produce the scientific equipment that has become part of modern society. The trained men who control the processes have had their minds educated and drilled for this purpose. 'Management therefore has a challenge and an obligation deliberately to plan and create a favourable, constructive attitude on the part of the wife that will liberate her husband's total energies for the job.' This is surely the rigid demand for conformity pinching a man in a sensitive and intimate area. As Packard quotes from the *Harvard Business Review*: 'Because of his (the scientist, engineer, or technologist in control) single-minded concentration on his job, even his sexual activity is relegated to a secondary place.'

Of course not all the citizens of advanced communities allow the persuasive influence of the 'scientific' mode of thinking to harm their love affairs. There is room along the road of scientific progress for the enjoyment of the goods that science can bring. It is not inevitable for the pursuit of productivity to damage the warm thoughts and feelings of humanity. But technological thinking upon which competitive productivity depends is pervasive. Love brings sadness. And even if we allow love perhaps to escape the too rigid grasp of science, what of sadness?

> Sadness, divine melancholy—
> Whose saintly visage is too bright
> To hit the sense of human sight,
> And therefore to our weaker view
> O'erlaid with black, staid Wisdom's hue.

In these modern times our minds have been conditioned to think differently from that of John Milton who saw some virtue and, indeed, pleasure to be had from sadness. A page of the current number of the *Journal of the Royal Society of Medicine* is devoted to an announcement of the effect of phenelzine, made up in 15-milligram tablets. These are the modern answer to a mind afflicted by 'nervousness', 'tension', 'fatigue states' and 'sadness' as well as 'insomnia', 'apprehension', 'irritability' and 'hypochondriasis'. This is the way we have brought ourselves to think in our modern world. Sadness and melancholy are no longer a part of life where, musing pensively, we may come to wisdom. The constant pressure of the affairs of applied science has been such that we now believe that these moods can be effectively dealt with by taking 15-milligram tablets of phenelzine, 'a true anti-depressant which relieves the depression-induced anxiety by alleviating the depression itself'.

The weight and the success of science press on the mind. Intelligent men may think they know that to accept scientific technology entire as a philosophy for living is to restrict the diversity and purpose of life. Yet intelligent men must conform to the daily routine, the export drive, and the rules of industrial society. They may think they know that sadness is not always amenable to phenelzine but they cannot deny that science has many remarkable successes to its credit. Men of the seventeenth century as intelligent as themselves wrote 'Lord have mercy on our souls' over their doors. Today the plague is understood and has been abolished by scientific methods. If it was the plague yesterday, can those who have sacrificed much to modern scientific technology—their time, their behaviour, their choice of a wife, and their way of thinking—be blamed for assuming that sadness too can be scientifically disposed of? And so we find the doctors of the 1960s reading in their conservative *Journal of the Royal Society of Medicine* an announcement by the British distributing agency of a great American pharmaceutical manufacturer to this effect. People who are 'depressed, unhappy, morose' need be so no longer. Nialamide is the specific therapy for these conditions. Take it, says the announcement, and you will find 'increased cheerfulness and hope'.

The citizen of the world of modern rationalism is faced by a very real dilemma. Let us assume that he has not yet become tied down to the doctrine of materialism to such an extent that his mind has become bent to accept that while 'there is nothing good or bad but thinking makes it so' nevertheless the good and bad he does think are explicable in scientific terms. Let us allow, I say, that he has not yet come to think this. He still accepts the view that a man may have human reasons for sadness and joy and may accept—free from chemical considerations—the delights of good and the misery of bad. At the same time this humanistic person about whom I am writing

knows too that madness is merely a peculiar accentuation of
sanity, that Shakespeare could truly ask 'What is madness
but to be mad?' He also knows—or can be told—that a mind
disturbed, 'a sick mind' as it would be called today, or one
afflicted by some degree of madness, as would have been said
in more outspoken times, can often be made to snap back into
its normal function, as does a dislocated shoulder, by the
administration to the patient of intravenous doses of barbitur-
ates. Other scientists have treated mentally afflicted people
with ether, excited them to the point of collapse and, when they
opened their eyes, their minds have been restored again. Other
chemical substances have been used with varying results:
laughing gas (nitrous oxide), methedrine and mixtures of
carbon dioxide and oxygen gas.

'To change behaviour patterns of thought and action in the
human brain with speed and efficiency', wrote Dr William
Sargent in 1957, 'it is apparently in many cases necessary to
induce some form of physiological brain disturbance.' And the
intelligent but not yet fully committed citizen knows that the
modern scientific forms of physiological brain disturbance that
are applied in practice are electric shocks passed through the
brain so as to induce artificial epileptic fits—'once or twice
weekly in courses of four to ten fits'—or large doses of insulin
sufficient to induce mental confusion and excitement followed
by deep coma. Or 'prefrontal leucotomy', a type of surgical
interference of the brain invented in 1936 by E. Moniz, a
Portuguese neurologist, and for which he received the highest
scientific award of a Nobel Prize, can be carried out. All these
procedures have produced a great deal of good; many afflicted
people have been relieved of their distress. Minds previously
fixed in their convictions or delusions have been changed and
made malleable. Faced with these scientific facts, the citizen of
today can hardly fail to submit to the environment in which he
lives and accept the general opinion of matter-of-fact people
that thoughts and opinions and beliefs, even sadness and joy,
are explicable in technological terms.

We've got it on the Brain

From time to time in history there have been heated theological arguments between those who assert that animals can go to heaven when they die and those who are equally convinced that the lower orders of creation are not permitted there. People who have become fond of their pets have let it be known that they themselves will refuse to pass through the pearly gates if they are not allowed to bring their dogs with them, while those of the opposite persuasion insist that creation can be divided into two parts: the brute beasts who will perish and humankind. The insidious and powerful pressure of the modern doctrine that applied science is national common sense is bending people's minds to accept that the thinking of thoughts, the conception of ideas, the birth of hope and fear and joy and distress—all these are products of a cerebral mechanism, and that the minds of dogs and men are subject to the same manipulations.

These manipulations were devised by the Russian physiologist, Pavlov, who died in 1936 at the age of eighty-six. His early observations are well known. Teach a dog to expect its dinner every time a lamp lights up and in due course the connection between light and food becomes fixed in its mind and its mouth will water when the lamp goes on, whether there is any dinner or not. Training of this kind can be applied to the minds of men as well as dogs; a practised cyclist rides a bicycle successfully 'without thinking'; a competent pianist can react 'automatically' to the marks on the page of music in front of him; a baby can be taught to pass water at the touch of a cold pot on its buttocks. But Pavlov's more advanced work on the mechanistic working of the brain was done later in life and its influence of all others bites most savagely on the minds of half the world's population.

It is a simple scientific experiment to 'condition' a dog to expect food when it feels a weak electric current run through its leg. The current itself is almost pleasurable—do not children play with 'shock' machines in fun fairs?—and its association with feeding makes it more so. But then the experimenter, bit by bit and day by day, increases the voltage of the current. Sharp and revolting pain is the price to be paid for food. The mind of the dog, tortured with pain and fear and hope and bewilderment, eventually breaks down.

This rather gruesome experiment was performed on a number of occasions and in a number of ways. A dog could be trained to expect food when a certain signal was given, for example, when a light was turned on or a buzzer buzzed. The connection between the signal and the reward was patiently and laboriously built up in its mind. But then Pavlov began to make the dog wait. The buzzer would sound or the light go on but there was a delay before the expected meal appeared. And this delay was made longer and longer. There was the dog, hungry and tired, the learned signal received—and it had to wait, tense, frustrated, slavering with anticipation, disappointed in its deepest hopes. Until at last its mind gave way again.

Or a dog trained to know that a light meant food and a buzzer meant a blast of cold air would one day find that the cold blast sometimes—only sometimes, mark you—blew when what had always before been the kindly light shone out. This too would eventually drive it to distraction.

Not all dogs allowed their minds to give way under these stresses. Some of them were tough-minded. They had given their hearts, as we say, and their devotion in learning how to behave, and worries and frustrations—even the confusing effects of the unexpected—did not make them change. But Pavlov, the diligent and committed scientist, elaborated more and more thorough experiments until he found a way of breaking down the coherent behaviour that he had before taken just as much trouble to build up. His final set of trials was a repetition of the earlier ones. He would gradually make a signal hurt the dog more and more painfully; he would delay longer and longer to provide the reward with which the signal had been linked in the creature's mind; he would confuse the signals which the dog had learned to associate with rewards with those previously associated with pains; and he would sound the bells meaning food and the buzzers meaning electric shocks and the horns warning against blasts of cold air faster and faster so that the dogs would dash about their cages in a frenzy of uncertainty. But for those of the dogs whose minds still remained inviolate even under the stress of this scientific pandemonium he reserved a final treatment. These animals would be castrated, or infected by fever, or given diarrhoea, and then the bells were made to ring, the buzzers to buzz, the horns to blow and the electric currents to shock. Then, at last, Pavlov found that his scientific experiments were successful, that he had discovered in quantitative terms the degree of stress required to remove a set of ideas from a dog's mind. There were, of course, further refinements and complexities by which he measured the means for printing new ideas in place of those he had erased, but the main point that he had established was the principle that impressions can be incised into a mind and removed from it by practical scientific means just as they can on a metal plate.

The good citizen of today accepts from the materialistic atmosphere of economic productivity the idea that not only can ideas and thoughts and inspirations and the evanescent dreams of freedom and justice and hope and beauty be explained in technological terms but that they ought to be explained so. The structure of a man's brain is not dissimilar from that of a dog, and it has—alas—already been shown that when it is subjected to the same kinds of stresses and tortures as those used in Pavlov's scientific experiments on dogs it behaves in exactly the same way: it breaks down, the ideas previously written on it are erased and new ones can, at the will of the experimenter, be imposed on the surface made blank.

We modern people have come to believe that the methods of the Inquisition were horrible. For a start, they were unscientific. Nevertheless, the tortures and imprisonment and the ceaseless questioning were an application in a rough and ready empirical form of the techniques later scientifically developed for dogs by Pavlov. And the purpose of the Inquisitors, although we may consider it to have been misguided, was a noble one. It was to bring the minds of the people they were working on back to a belief in the true faith, without which they would not only be deprived of the felicities of Heaven but would find themselves subject to the far more painful and prolonged tortures of Hell. The object of the technique applied by the inquisitors was to change people's minds. Their methods were unscientific and sometimes—but not always—unsuccessful because the environmental pressures of those days, whatever they may have implied about the nature of God, were based on the assumption that men's minds were reflections of individual living souls. Today, the scientific atmosphere brings us to think that, in men as in dogs, minds are mechanisms of a certain sort that can be impressed with ideas in a certain way and, if required, can be broken down in another certain way so that the set of ideas on them can be taken off and new ones put on.

The methods elaborated in his physiological laboratory by Pavlov for dogs have been quite successfully adapted for men under the loose term of 'brain-washing'. The experiments on dogs were carried out to advance scientific knowledge of the mechanism and structure of the mind. We are today agreed that the acquisition of accurate knowledge is good. This being so, the hardship inflicted on the dogs—our minds have been moulded to say—was justified by the ends achieved. It was in just such a spirit that minds shaped by the quite different pressures of mediaevalism accepted without question that 'primrose paths' did inevitably lead to 'the everlasting bonfire', and that this bonfire was real and did really burn and consume with real flames the bodies of the damned. The momentary discomforts of the rack and the thumb-screws and the stake were, therefore, as justifiable as were the sufferings of Pavlov's dogs.

Dogs and long dead heretics may not excite the interest of the less imaginative members of today's society. But for us to-day there is still time to consider whether we wish to challenge the idea that human brains are only complex mechanisms, something like automatic telephone exchanges, and that they can be manipulated and reorganised and disconnected just as easily. And even if the scientific evidence forces us to accept that brains can be manipulated, are we also to agree that they should be, so that their owners can be more smoothly fitted into the community to make it more efficient in producing industrial wealth?

The literature of the technique of 'brain-washing' is quite extensive. This is not altogether to be wondered at since the process has now been applied comparatively widely. There are available accounts of its being applied in Russia and countries of Eastern Europe, in China, Korea and elsewhere. Those authors who have studied the matter, Dr William Sargent, for example, or Dr J. A. Meerloo, implicitly accept the basic assumption that a man's mind is a machine that can be stopped in such-and-such a way and put into reverse by the use of such-and-such a technique. And although minds vary in strength and come in different sizes, it has to be accepted that no mind is immune to the influences studied in detailed and quantitative terms by Pavlov during the course of his somewhat disagreeable series of animal experiments. This conclusion is one more indication of the general conformity to the doctrine that society's purpose is technology, and that since the minds of nonconformists can be made to conform by technological methods it is not unreasonable that they should be made to do so.

But though science can be used to change minds, though it has to be admitted that a mind is a machine that can be broken down, that in fact any mind, no matter how loyal or strong or brave, can be brought to the point of unsaying the convictions and beliefs to which it has always held and made to profess beliefs and ideas that it previously abhorred—whether it be the mind of a Cardinal Mindszenty of Hungary or Colonel Schwable of the United States Marines—in spite of all this and in spite of the persuasive pressure to believe that the purpose of modern society is no absenteeism and increased industrial productivity, there are still people whose lives follow a different path.

We have already considered the devout millions in India purifying themselves in the waters of the Ganges. And we too in the industrial West can find many who quietly and without sentimental fuss love one dog as a friend. These people do not see dogs as 'material' for psychological research or test organisms for space rockets. And they have not yet joined the stream of those who see a nation's aim in terms of productivity. Here and there are artists and dreamers, a very few philosophers, and even some who cling to ideas of noble deeds and honourable action apart altogether from technological efficiency. Dotted about in our society are those whose standards of life are distinct altogether from the 'standard of living'.

The idea that industrial output and industrial progress are the whole end of man can be opposed without undue pain even if those people who resist may suffer some loss of income and social acceptability in commercial and governmental circles. But Dr Meerloo, who was once Chief of the Psychological Department of the Netherlands armed forces and now teaches psychiatry at Columbia University, has also good advice for those who want to resist the forces investigated so efficiently by Pavlov. Dr Meerloo does not deny that scientific knowledge is now available by which any mind can be overwhelmed. Hunger, lack of sleep, ill-usage and constant skilled repetition, repetition, repetition, mixed appropriately with unkindness, kindness and unkindness—exactly as applied to the laboratory dogs—will in the end make any mind admit that black is white if this is the purpose of the operation. But there is no special cause for despair about this. Industrial society is widely equipped with machinery that destroys the bodies of those who use it, whether the machinery takes the form of thermonuclear weapons or automobiles on the highway. Why then should we be alarmed at the equally effective techniques that are capable of disrupting minds? Men and women have been found prepared to confront the physical force of science. Dr Meerloo points out that the great and courageous minds for the future who will defy both the spirit of conformity implicit in materialism and the highly efficient practical processes that are also now available to make them conform will be those possessed of spiritual bravery.

In a different world Galileo brought his mind to the point of dissent from the accepted framework of thought; Newton boldly conceived laws of motion that brought the heavens and the earth into a single system comprehensible to human minds by the logic of mathematics. The pervasiveness of technology, its material success, its effectiveness when applied directly to mould men's minds, may of itself call forth the modern heroism: the strength to dissent courageously.

The present environment that presses so strongly on the corporate mind of modern Western communities is comparatively new. Its present shape may change. We may have second thoughts about the value of the glittering material prizes it is giving us. Perhaps the people who work it may themselves suffer a change of mind because they too are new to the purpose that they now serve. Dr Bowden of the Manchester College of Science and Technology has made some interesting calculations on this point. It seems that the number of scientists and technologists in the world has doubled every fifteen years since the time of Newton. This means that three-quarters of all the scientists and technologists who ever lived are still alive today. It is just possible that perhaps they have not quite realised yet what it is they are trying to do.

5

PUFF, PUFF, PUFF

THE BISHOP of Bristol was one day sitting in a London tram-car when an elegant gentleman, dressed in the full splendour of English respectability—pin-striped trousers, bowler hat and immaculately-rolled umbrella—got in and sat down beside him. There was on the opposite seat a small boy who, after scrutinising the newcomer for a full two minutes without speaking, turned to his mother and asked in a peculiarly pene-trating treble tone (or so the Bishop tells it), 'Mummy, what's that man for?'

What answer the boy received to his question the Bishop never said. In fact, as an apparently prosperous member of a technological society the main purpose of which is to produce industrial good in ever-increasing amounts, what he was for (apart from doing his share in producing the goods) was to accept his responsibilities as a citizen and consume his due share of goods too. In fact, his very presence in the tramcar must be taken as a fault, since it would have been better for the economic health of the automobile industry had he been driving a car instead. We might add that the Bishop himself was in an equivocal position as well, because one of the things bishops are for—it could be argued—is to encourage a prosperous society with confidence in its own aims.

Obviously the Bishop, if he was a good bishop, might not necessarily accept the pressures of modern prosperous nations —that life was meant for a buoyant market and rising pro-ductivity—nevertheless Advertising (with a capital 'A'), which is one of the major pressures, is without doubt clearly aimed to this end. It is interesting to see that, just as the assumptions of technological society as a whole (that productivity is Good) are accepted without question and pursued by scientific means, so also does Advertising know that it is good and pursue its ends scientifically.

Mr P. G. Wodehouse in 1923 wrote a fable in which one of his characters, a well-born young man, was anxious to persuade his uncle, on whom he was financially dependent, to consent to his marriage to a maiden in humble circumstances who worked in a teashop. The proposed solution to the problem was described by Jeeves in the following terms:

'The method which I advocate is what, I believe, the advertisers call Direct Suggestion, sir, consisting as it does of driving an idea home by constant repetition. You may have had experience of the system?'

'You mean they keep on telling you that some soap or other is the best, and after a bit you come under the influence and charge round the corner and buy a cake?'

'Exactly, sir. The same method was the basis of all the most valuable propaganda during the recent war.'*

This is a simple description of a straightforward process for impressing an idea on the public mind. It is scientific at least to the extent that any direct learning process is scientific. The idea to be conveyed is repeated again and again. 'Stephens Ink', 'Stephens Ink'. At one time wherever one went in the British Isles there was an enamelled metal sign simply repeating 'Stephens Ink'. The sign went into no further detail. It made no effort to say anything about the ink: it simply reiterated the name.

Another charming example of the same genre, slightly more elaborate perhaps and, in relying on versification, perhaps a whit more artistic but giving no particular technical information, was once again a widely-distributed sign, antique versions

* From 'Jeeves Exerts the Old Cerebellum', in *The Inimitable Jeeves*. (Herbert Jenkins.)

of which may still be found on tumble-down brick walls. It ran like this:

> They come as a boon and a blessing to men,
> The Pickwick, the Owl and the Waverley pen.

Nowadays this method of attack would be considered naïve but it is, nevertheless, soundly based. Gentle and persistent hammering gradually produces an impression. It is not necessary to do more than make a name familiar. 'Pear's Soap', says the announcement again and again, 'Pear's Soap'. And even if the message given is in the form of a sentence, it need not mean anything. All that is necessary is to keep up a continuous din so that wherever a man may turn, there, beating away like ritual drums in the jungle, will be the repeated refrain: 'Beer is Best', 'Beer is Best', 'Beer is Best'. (It is not necessary to state under what circumstances it is best.) And widely-spread pill advertisements claiming over and over again: 'worth a guinea a box', do not seriously expect to be taken at their face value.

It should perhaps be noted that no experienced advertiser would propose, except under quite remarkable and unusual circumstances, to frame an advertisement merely to describe the article for sale, with an account of what it is for, what it will do, and what it costs. This would be unscientific. For the most part, the purpose of advertising is to persuade a person to buy what he does not want and not to select what he does want. Since this is so, it is only reasonable for advertisers to apply scientific pressures in order to get him to do so. The scientific method of applying pressure can be made to work just as well when the advertising, if taken literally, is untrue as when it is half true, or even absolutely accurate. This happens because sophisticated modern advertising, just like the simple old-fashioned 'guinea a box' approach, does not depend primarily on what it explicitly says.

And so we find the citizen of our modern civilization being subjected to pressure in the form of meaningless combinations of words; for example, being urged over and over again to

smoke a particular brand of cigarette, not because of any des-
cribable quality or characteristic but because of some quite
irrelevant, and often incomprehensible, quality. Or he is
pressed and pressed again to use a toothpaste because it contains a named substance of which he had previously never
heard and of whose significance he is entirely ignorant. This
is pressure in an effective but sematically neutral form. This
kind of thing is, of course, capable of infinite extension when
the article which the advertisement is designed to sell is pressed
on the consciousness of the consumer connected by a web of
words and pictures with anything else under the sun no matter
how far removed from the article itself. The toothpaste, washing powder, underclothing or motorcar can be impressed on
the consciousness of its putative consumer on the basis of its
content of the incomprehensible additive, its alleged connection with health, beautiful girls, prosperous people, funny
animals or fresh sea breezes. The scientific principle elucidated
by Pavlov implied that the mind of a dog could be 'conditioned'
to connect by constant repetition the idea of food with the
word 'dinner' or, for that matter, with the word 'omnibus' or
with an entirely meaningless sound such as a bell or a hooter or
two pieces of wood rubbing together. And to impress a simple
idea on a man's mind too, it is not strictly necessary to use
words conveying meaning.

Half-true ideas suggesting goodness and attractiveness in
general terms are sometimes used to support the action of the
process of reiteration on the minds of readers. These ideas are
not strictly intended to convey accurate meaning. No one who
resists the psychological impact of the advertising process long
enough to think would actually believe that a grotesque vehicle
in lacquered steel is 'the most beautiful, the sleekest, the most
transcendental' object ever created, but the fact that the word-
ing of the motorcar advertisement says so may serve to
flavour the impression that it makes on the reader's mind.
Similarly, expressions like 'inner cleanliness' when applied to
a laxative, although void of meaning, convey an impression of

desirability which is possibly one degree stronger than the description of a cigarette as being 'toasted'. Similarly, meaningless pejorative statements such as 'flavour blur' or 'night starvation' can be used to impress people's minds favourably towards the articles alleged to overcome these imaginary ills.

This being an age when science and technology are powerful agents of our modern society and are, therefore, treated with the respect which their importance demands, it is not surprising that the words used in advertisements often possess a scientific flavour. In this way the impression to be produced by the constant repetition, which is the basis of the advertising process, is reinforced by the prestige attached to the idea of science.

In the early 1950s a powerful pressure of advertising was brought to bear on the consumers of the Western world to purchase a wide variety of goods to which chlorophyll had been added, on the basis that this substance would prevent the user from smelling. The articles in question ranged from toothpaste, soap and sugar confectionery all the way to socks, bedlinen, whisky and wallpaper. And the volume of trade—a great wave blown up by a powerful and sustained blast of advertising—was very large.

Chlorophyll is the chemical compound which gives the greenness to grass and leaves. It is the basis for the life of mankind and all the higher animals because, using the energy in the light of the sun as motive power, it links up the carbon dioxide gas in the atmosphere with water to form sugars from which all vegetable food (and so all animal food) is derived. The fact that chlorophyll is capable of doing this remarkable thing— that is, using the physical energy of light to work a *chemical* process—means that it is a substance of outstanding biochemical importance which has been deeply studied by serious scientists. Apart from researches into the way it works in green leaves, its possible effect on all sorts of biological systems has been investigated.

In 1937 and 1938 reports began to appear in Swiss medical

literature that chlorophyll stimulated the healing of wounds. It is rather doubtful whether this effect can stand up to close scrutiny, and its significance compared to the enormous and fundamental importance of the basic function of chlorophyll in photosynthesis is trivial, even if it exists at all. In 1940 an American scientific paper was published stating that it caused the smell of suppurations to disappear. Further experiments were carried out in the U.S.A., and in 1949 scientists at the University of Pennsylvania reported, amongst other details of their experiment, that 'for eleven patients where the observation was made, the smell of wounds of seven was reduced'.

By now the possible relationship between chlorophyll and smell had begun to attract attention. In 1950 a report was published in a United States medical journal entitled 'Oral chlorophyll fractions for body and breath deodorisation'. This gave the details of an investigation in which tablets of chlorophyll derivatives were given by mouth and the effect on various body smells examined. Here is an example. Twelve people who had been eating onions were given 100 mg. chlorophyll tablets. After two hours, the smell of onions could no longer be detected in the breath of four of them, and was described as 'barely detectable' in that of a fifth. But in the other seven of the twelve people in the trial, the smell of onions was still present in their breath after four hours.

This then was the type of evidence which convinced the people who were technically concerned with the production of dentrifrices and air-conditioners, mouthwash and tablets to cure bad breath that chlorophyll added to these articles would increase sales—whether or not it exerted any useful effect in suppressing smell. Soon, under the hammer, hammer, hammer of the pressure of advertising, now expressed in seemingly scientific terms, chlorophyll preparations were being sold in America on such a scale that the manufacturers were obliged to import large quantities of chlorophyll from the British Isles where it was produced as a by-product of the grass-drying industry.

And belief in the efficacy of chlorophyll as being of assistance in social life was accepted—at least for the period the advertising pressure continued. Indeed, at one time the governor of a gaol in one of the southern states of the U.S.A. was reported as forbidding the inmates under his charge to use chlorophyll preparations of any kind—even toothpaste—for fear that if they escaped the bloodhounds might not find sufficient scent to pick up their trail.

Rational thought has never been a certain protection against the pressure waves blown up by the forces of advertising backed by experience and science. For example, if chlorophyll —a substance shown years ago in 1939 by Professor Elvehjem of the University of Wisconsin to be not even absorbed into the human body when eaten—if chlorophyll should affect the body's smell, how would it be expected to act? The smell of a human body is mainly due to bacterial decomposition of sebaceous secretions—that is to say, sweat—on the skin. Thinking would suggest that there are two ways of diminishing the intensity of such smell; either by removing periodically these secretions from the skin—by having a bath, for example —or by preventing bacterial decomposition taking place. But according to an authoritative statement made by the American Medical Association in 1951, there was no evidence that chlorophyll decreases this secretion or that it alters the kind of bacteria normally found on the skin.

Thinking might also bring forward the following considerations about the smell of breath which—it was insisted again and again with pressure exerted this way and that way— chlorophyll tablets and properly treated whisky (containing 'colourless' chlorophyll) could improve or abolish. The facts are that only a small part of the smell of breath comes from the mouth and teeth (the only parts accessible to chlorophyll toothpaste, for example), and this can be removed fairly easily. Breath is the exhaust of the bodily engine. And just as the smell of the exhaust of a car does not come from the exhaust pipe but from the products of combustion of petroleum in the engine,

so with breath the smell comes from the products of combustion of the body's fuel transported by the blood and dis-
charged into the lungs. For example, when a person has been
drinking, alcohol and other ingredients of the drinks pass into
the blood stream. Alcohol is only slowly combustible, and
since it is volatile a significant proportion of it will also be
present in the breath. Indeed, the amount of alcohol in breath
is a measure of the amount of drink taken. It follows, therefore, that to the experienced observer the smell of alcohol in
breath cannot be concealed merely by washing out the mouth
or by sucking a chlorophyll tablet.

Thoughts about garlic make the proposed miraculous operation of chlorophyll even more difficult to accept. People who
eat garlic regularly store a proportion of its odoriferous
principle in their livers from whence it can pass into the blood
stream and thence, via the lungs, into the breath. It can also
pass through the skin. In an experimental trial, garlic was
rubbed on to the soles of a boy's feet; the substance carrying
the smell passed through the skin of his feet into his blood
stream and then, in the ordinary course of the circulation of the
blood, into the lungs. Within an hour of the beginning of the
experiment his breath smelled of garlic.

The tide rose. The pressure to use products containing
chlorophyll to suppress smell became stronger and stronger.
It was maintained partly by the hammer, hammer, hammer
of repetition and partly by the persuasive implication that
Science showed that this was a good and effective thing to do.
Throughout, the American Medical Association was doubtful.
'Not only is the mechanism of action (of chlorophyll) unex-
plained,' it reported, 'but it is not at all certain that the action
exists except in the mind of the observer.' Then the tide ebbed.
Nothing was said, but green toothpaste gradually turned back
to white (with perhaps a red stripe in it) and the pressure of
Advertising turned to maximise the consumption of some other
industrial product in some other way.

In our technological communities the goal of high industrial

'. . . *garlic can also pass through the skin . . .*'

production must, it seems—since we are unable so far to find ways of transmitting our products across the boundaries of latitude and ethnology—be matched, as an equally important goal, by higher and higher consumption. Hence, the advertisers whose business it is to make us achieve this ever rising standard of consumption find it tempting to go on using what may seem to be 'science' even though incidents like the rise and fall of chlorophyll may occur.

A pharmaceutical manufacturer, for example, publishes a full-page advertisement designed to show why everyone ought to take their vitamin pills. The tone of the text was that of a public-spirited organisation trying to perform a social duty by putting the facts about vitamins before the public. And the burden of the argument was that since official national surveys show that the vitamin content of typical diets is sometimes below the minimum recommended intake, therefore, to be on the safe side, everyone might well spend a small sum each day on a multipurpose vitamin pill to protect himself and his family. Scientific and medical experts in the United States find this type of advertisement disturbing, not because, as the Government and the American Medical Association experts agreed it was, 'the ad. was scientific hokum', but because the public were subjected to substantial pressure but might not recognise that they were being impressed by an advertisement.

It is now generally accepted that the force of Advertising need not depend on what the advertisement says in words, whether true, half-true or untrue. The journal *Science* comments almost as a platitude that 'nearly all over-the-counter (that is, non-prescription) drug advertising is to some extent misleading'. For example, during an epidemic of Asian influenza it may seem effective advertising for a manufacturer of a laxative to print: 'If you have Asian 'flu and need a laxative take . . .' Another pharmaceutical manufacturer may use—and find it helpful to his sales and distribution to do so—the approach: 'If you have cancer and need a headache remedy, take ——'s aspirin.' In the British Isles, where the chilly climate together with the inability of the local inhabitants to take the necessary steps to warm their houses combine to induce a high incidence of colds during the winter months, newspaper advertisements, television and posters alike all press the Briton with the slogan: 'Don't take cold, take——'s vitamin capsules.' The prestige of science may be said to back up this instruction on the basis that because the eyeballs of rats deprived of vitamin A become dry and consequently susceptible to infection, and because in many instances the dried-up corneas of their eyes do become infected, it is therefore justifiable to consider vitamin A to be an anti-infective vitamin. And because for this reason it acts as an anti-infective agent to protect the corneas of vitamin-A-deficient rats' eyes, it can also be assumed to protect well-fed men and women against the cold virus.

Advertising is one of the legitimate pressures that are exerted upon the citizenry of Western technological societies. The unwritten principles of the American Federal Trade Commission seem to be that it is not the business of the government to insure that advertisements always tell the truth or that they are only used to press the consumer to buy what will in fact do him good. But what the F.T.C. would like to do would be to establish as one of the rules of the game the principle that people ought to be able at least to know when an advertisement is an advertisement.

It will be interesting to see whether in the end this one office of the national government of the United States, a country as rigidly conformist to industrial efficiency as any other, will be able to escape this form of pressure. Advertising, that serves so important a function in 'advanced' communities, has itself adopted a 'scientific' approach and this approach is giving advertisements many and diverse forms.

It was soon apparent that if one man would buy an article because an advertisement described it clearly and unemotionally as something he wanted, ten men would buy it because they had seen its name ceaselessly repeated wherever they went. But compared with the ten, a hundred would come in response to an advertisement that appealed to some hidden, unconscious urge they never knew they possessed. As Packard in his book has pointed out, advertisers have discovered that the citizens of the modern scientific state are not moved by reason when they respond to an advertisement. Instead of the rational creatures they believe themselves to be, they are 'bundles of daydreams, misty hidden yearnings, guilt complexes, irrational emotional blockages'. This being so, the advertisers have set themselves, as scientifically as they know how, to appeal to their customers' unrecognised feelings rather than to their intelligence.

By drawing on the knowledge and experience of psychologists and social scientists the advertisers hope to be able to elucidate the real motives that impel a man or woman to buy one brand of cigarette rather than another or—for that matter —to buy cigarettes at all. This is, perhaps, not the place to delve into the pharmacological effects of the common social drugs: alcohol, caffeine and theobromine in tea and coffee, and nicotine in tobacco. The nicotine does demonstrably exert an effect, there is some degree of pleasurable stimulation, and it has actually been claimed that the transient sensation of nausea, most forcibly apparent to new smokers and those who indulge in strong chewing tobacco or powerful cigars, is itself attractive to certain people. Nevertheless, it is very striking that although in logic it might be assumed that the magnitude and the precise nature of the physiological effect exerted by a cigarette would be the main characteristics of interest to those who bought them, these qualities are never referred to by advertisers. They are undoubtedly important. During World War II when pipe tobacco was extremely expensive in Great Britain and not very easy to obtain, an enterprising manufacturer marketed, at an extremely attractive low price, a 'herb tobacco'. This material smouldered satisfactorily in the bowl of a pipe and produced blue smoke of attractive appearance with an aromatic aroma vaguely reminiscent of a distant bonfire. But being free from the drug, nicotine, smoking it was entirely without interest.

It would be logical for an advertiser to tell his potential customers just how much pharmacological potency his cigarettes contain. It would be logical but it is never done because modern studies in 'motivational research' have suggested that people smoke cigarettes for many reasons, among which their physiological potency is not particularly important. Packard described a 'thorough depth study' of 350 American smokers from which the investigators deduced that people smoke to show that they are manly and mature; young smokers are unconsciously demonstrating that they are fully grown up and older people, particularly women, smoke to show that they are young and still in the prime of their vigour too. It is not surprising, therefore, to find cigarette advertisements showing a handsome young couple strolling hand in hand through the fields (with the right cigarettes), or looking out to sea together through the blustering wind (smoking), or, with their horses's bridles loosely hanging from their arms, wandering through the woods while he holds his lighter for her to draw upon. There is no word about the quality of the cigarettes, their price, whether they cause smokers' cough, cancer of the lung, or if they taste of Latakia. The impression the advertisement strives to produce on the minds of those who see it is that people who buy the brand are young, sporty and successful with the opposite sex

The advertisers nowadays are paying more attention to their customers' supposed 'unconscious' than they do to a straightforward description of the goods they have to sell. They try to deduce the state of internal conflict going on in a potential buyer's mind between his id, his ego and his super-ego. Motorcar manufacturers, for example, began to realise that the rated horse-power of their vehicles, their performance on the road, whether or not they could go round a corner at fifty miles an hour without swaying and squealing and the ease with which they could be stopped in an emergency had very little to do with whether they could be sold or not. Most of the people bought one kind of car rather than another because it satisfied their idea of the figure they would cut in front of their friends and acquaintances. The ornamentation of cars in the United States with large, heavy, inconvenient and often dangerous tail-fins was not entirely stupidity on the part of the manufac-turers, even though anyone with a vestige of artistic taste could instantly recognise that the fins were ugly and did not, therefore, even serve the purpose of decoration. Their installation did, however, inflate for a while the self-esteem of the car owners. Packard cites an even more extreme example of this kind of scientific approach to human motives in an account of the importance to sales of another quite useless attribute to a motorcar; the noise of its door slamming. He quotes the *New York Herald Tribune*'s account of the seven-man panel of psychological experts employed by the Chevrolet Company to evaluate the 'psychological overtones' of the sound and smell of different car models. These experts attached especial signi-ficance to the door slam. If ever the congestion on the high-ways forces motorcar manufacturers to sell for town use really small cars, we can confidently expect, if advertising science has its way, that as the customers are stripped of the pomposity of their huge overhangs, as one by one they lose first the tail fins, then the great grinning grill at the front, then the lavish seating, accommodating three adults and a dog side by side, the diminutive vehicle that will eventually be left will at least possess a three-tone horn like a Cadillac and its doors will slam with the hushed ostentation of the portals of a baronial hall.

The attack of the advertisers on the unconscious mind of their victims has been organised with great diligence. For example, it is often found to increase the consumption of an article—and this, after all, is the purpose—by using an adver-tisement that talks about some aspect of the product, prefer-ably in a scientific way, so that the purchasers think that they are influenced by what is said. In fact, they are yielding to quite a different motive. The toothpaste people have over the years impressed on the public how disastrous it can be if bacteria are allowed to attack the teeth. The toothpaste advertisements have constantly been full of reference to mystical ingredients which can save teeth from the attacks of the deadly microbes. In fact, while gaining a comfortable feeling of scientific rectitude from being told about these 'Milestones in Modern Medicine', the various toothpastes hold their popularity largely from their taste and the sensation of freshness they provide when people clean their teeth—as almost all of them do—when they get up in the morning. Immediately afterwards they eat their breakfast and build up a handsome load of bacteria throughout the day and on through the night until the following morning. Although it is nowadays not a common cause of injury, *Mordus humani*—a human bite—still produces a notoriously dangerous wound due to the likelihood of infection. As customarily used by the normal citizen, toothpaste, whether it contains a mystic antiseptic or not, does not to any material extent of itself reduce the concentration of micro-organisms in the mouth.

But the point which the advertisers have appreciated is that they can bring pressure to bear much more powerfully and effectively if they attack the unconscious desires of consumers. No longer is the reiteration on every hoarding 'Pear's Soap', 'Pear's Soap'. No longer is it considered useful to design a funny joke to attract attention to the name—in the early decades of the century a traditional tramp was depicted as writing, 'Ten years ago I used your soap, since then I've used no other.' Today, the soap manufacturers do not merely promise to make ladies clean, they promise to make them beautiful. The television sings the refrain, 'Look your loveliest' with someone-or-other's soap. For men, it is a promise of strength and virility—and a smell, too, guaranteed to bring the ladies swarming. The motor manufacturers do not sell just a car, they sell status and prestige.

It is perhaps a little remarkable to realise that efficient

advertisers bring to bear their specialised pressures, based to a marked degree on 'motivational research' and designed to entrap the unconscious mind of their customers, even when they are selling machinery and industrial equipment. It might be thought that if an engineer requires a hundred valves, let us say, fabricated out of stainless steel of a certain grade and each capable of handling 5000 gallons of liquid an hour he would invite quotations from a list of selected suppliers and choose the one most effectively meeting his specification at the lowest price. But this is not so. Even the industrial technologists who of all others are those who keep the Technological Society going—even these are men who can themselves be subjected to the quasi-scientific pressures of advertisement. Open any technical journal in the field of engineering or applied chemistry and physics and there once again are the dream-fulfilment archangels—the clean-limbed, impeccably dressed and always youthful characters. The advertisers of electric motors and turbines, of pumps and control valves, of electronic equipment and steam traps attempt to gain customers just as much by the process of flattering the unconscious dreams of the engineers and technologists who are their buyers as if they were nothing more than self-indulgent middle-aged housewives who are to be seduced into buying a box of chocolates by an advertisement suggesting that these chocolates are inevitably entangled with romantic love. The quality and specification of the particular pump or motor or steam trap will undoubtedly have some influence on the buyer; but, as with toothpaste and motorcars and aspirin tablets and soap, there is a good deal of competition in the market for technical equipment, and if an advertiser can dig into the buyer's mind so that he feels that he is particularly shrewd and astute by dealing with supplier A rather than supplier B, he will use every skill he may possess in order to get the buyer to do so.

An extension of the advertising pressures exerted on technical purchasers by imposing on their unconscious motives as well as appealing to their professional knowledge is the dissemination of a general atmosphere of optimism and prosperity. Advertisers will set themselves out to give the overworked purchasing officer of the great engineering combine the impression that he is astute and deeply read, and at the same time is the sort of man who wears good clothes, drives a stylish car, and—yes, even in some technical journals—has exciting and *chic* women friends. This of itself may persuade him to place his order for galvanised angle-iron with 'the right' firm. At the same time, however, the advertiser will also try to give the industrial buyer the impression that business is good and getting better, that the present is a good time to initiate new projects, and that everyone else knows this too. This added psychological pressure is projected on to the potential customer so that he may be prevented, not from buying from the wrong firm but from abstaining altogether.

A further oddity that has been discovered by psychological studies carried out into the deeper layers of the minds of customers for industrial equipment is that, not only do they respond to subtle flattery about their virility, astuteness, modernity and social status—just like purchasers of chocolates or shoes—and not only do they react to influences suggesting that *now* is the best time to invest in new industrial plant, but in addition their minds are full of quite a miscellany of technical prejudices and folk-lore that one would have imagined their technological education would have done away with during their student days. Perrin Stryker, for example, quotes the General Electric Company as having discovered during the course of 'motivational research' into the reactions of the readers of their technical advertisements, that there are quite large numbers of engineers who have it firmly fixed in their minds that direct-current electric motors are 'old fashioned'. And for this purely emotional reason they waste their own money and put the G.E.C. to a good deal of trouble adapting alternating-current motors to jobs in, for example, automatic processes, where direct-current motors actually do better. Other psychologists called in to examine the reluctance of engineers to install glass pipes for the transport of corrosive and chemically sensitive liquids found that their childhood memories of being scolded for breaking glass vessels at home had a sufficiently powerful influence over their unconscious minds to prevent their specifying glass in industrial contexts even when all the specifications—and the price as well— demonstrated that it was without question the most suitable material of construction. The advertising psychologists got round the problem—so they believed—by changing their text so that, instead of trying to convince the engineer that glass was actually very strong indeed (and having his unconscious mind wake him up at night with the repressed picture of an angry mother spanking him with a slipper for breaking a vase in the living room), the new copy released his psychological tensions by saying that although glass, with all its virtues, was breakable, although some people might break the industrial piping, a clever, well-qualified chap *like him* would get splendid results with it.

And so the pressures are developed more and more subtly by the advertisers, armed as they are with a new understanding of the deep motives that underlie the behaviour of men and women in everything they do. The advertisers up till now, however, have not employed their technical skills to exert pressure on quite *every* activity of the citizens of our technological society who are already conscribed within the rigidities of the modern scientific conformity. The main efforts of advertisers are designed to influence people's economic behaviour—that is, the things they buy. And they now know that when people buy hats, or cars, or food, or mouthwashes, a whole lot of considerations must be borne in mind other than whether the hats are durable and will keep their heads warm, and whether the cars will go properly, the food prove wholesome and the mouthwash effectively wash the mouth.

Why this apparently specialised kind of pressure that affects the modern citizen is worth discussing here at such length is that it is an essential corollary of the main movement of technological communities—that it is the purpose of each man and woman in the community to produce. Not to produce any specific thing but to produce anything so long as it can be consumed. The advertising pressure is an essential support of this main ethic of technological society. But we uncommitted people who have forborne as yet to take the path that leads to acceptable—if rigid—conformity and whose minds, we are so presumptuous as to assume, have not yet been deformed to fit—we may feel that what verges on a foul blow is being aimed, for example, at technical agriculturalists when the great expensive and complex machines that they must now buy for their large-scale operations are sold to them with different moving parts highly coloured according to a predetermined code. The up-to-date farmers are assured that there is an important technical reason for this colouring: that the colours indicate different parts of the mechanical system. The advertisers know that, in truth, there is no technical justification for the colours: they have been devised by psychologists to appeal to unconscious urges buried in the farmer's infancy.

We uncommitted strangers who wander in technological civilisation feel a mite appalled at Gerard Lambert's cheerful account in his book, *All out of Step*, of how cleverly he hit on halitosis as a peg to hang advertising on to sell enormous quantities of Listerine. And then when the force exerted by bad breath eventually began to flag he tells just as cheerfully how sales pressure was successfully maintained on the basis that Listerine would cure, first sore throat, then dandruff, and finally, that it could be marketed just as effectively as an after-shave lotion.

And perhaps there are old-fashioned people who question the pressure directed on to children so that after listening to advertisements on television they shall sing commercial jingles in praise of selected brands of beer, or acquire the fixed notion that Olympic champions owe their athletic prowess to the smoking of a particular brand of cigarettes, or even that it is good behaviour and fun as well to fill their mouths with hand-

fuls of a particular kind of sweetmeat. We have already discussed how children's education is directed to some degree at
least so that they may the more easily acquire later on technical
qualifications needed for good jobs in industry. If, then,
industry takes one part of their childhood thus to fit them for
production, we should not be surprised if advertising likewise
applies itself to children too in the cause of consumption. This
is what Professor David Potter of Yale has written about the
matter:

> Advertising is an instrument comparable to the school and
> the church in the extent of its influence upon society. . . .
> This influence will increase and, in the economies of
> abundance . . . advertising begins to fulfil a really essential
> economic function. In this situation the producer knows
> that the limitation upon his operations and upon his growth
> no longer lies . . . in his productive capacity, for he can
> always produce as much as the market will absorb. . . . If this
> new capacity is to be used, the imperative must fall upon
> consumption, and the society must be adjusted to a new set
> of drives and values in which consumption is paramount.'*

This is very clear and concise. This is, indeed, what the
pressure to conform, to be efficient and to raise the standard of
living are about: their purpose is to press men and women into
proper shape for production and consumption. It is the few
stray people who have not yet been shaped to size who wonder.
Advertising is an instrument comparable to the church, is it?
—but with a different purpose.

* From *The Amazing Advertising Business*. (Simon & Schuster, 1957.)

6

BACKWARDS WITH THE CLERGY

SCIENCE is a way of thinking. Applied to material objectives it has given us immense benefits, great wealth, clothes, food, luxuries and travel. Agricultural science has enormously increased the productivity of the earth and has raised the bent backs of all the multitude of Adam's sons who were condemned to eat bread in the sweat of their brows. Applied science has given us wings on which we can fly faster than the wind and which, in our own generation, will be capable of bearing us—how much more swiftly than the Ebony Horse—to the moon and the planets. The applied science which is the motive force of our society has given us comforts and pleasures, scents and sights unimagined by the Pharaohs and, as an extra reward, command over plague and pestilence as well. Great benefits, enormous good, have indeed come our way by this process of applying logical thought to the touchstone of Nature.

But then, to haunt us, we catch sight of the drawn faces of men and women—richer in material goods than their ancestors —as they hurry into the factories or drive tensely along congested highways. In the last hundred years we have perhaps learned to protect our bodies from the worst mutilations of mechanisation—we have invented pure air laws, and pure food laws, and factory acts, and trades unions, and we are even beginning to arm ourselves against being killed by automobiles—but what can we do to protect our minds?

Modern societies have thrown up a number of philosophical systems in line with their main ethics of productivity and efficiency. Marxism was, I suppose, a striking example of these; National Socialism was another. Free enterprise is perhaps a system of values that may still find favour in the West in spite of the wounds left by the slump of 1927. But some of the waverers who hesitate to press forward along the main road of technological productivity—with all the rich and tempting prizes it has so clearly to offer—still remember different goals: there was once humanitarianism . . . and liberalism . . . neighbourliness, too, as a guide to conduct. Perhaps the clergy, whose business, so Professor Potter of Yale is quoted as thinking, shares something with that of advertising, can help us to deal with applied science and use it as a way to the good life.

It is perhaps unfair to blame the clergy directly for the statement of the *Kölnische Zeitung* of 28 March 1819, that 'on theological grounds' they condemned the then newly-invented gas lighting 'because it appears to be an intervention in the divine order. According to the latter, night is appointed to be a darkness only broken at certain times by the moon. We ought not to rebel against this, we ought not to cavil at the cosmic plan and seek to turn night into day.' Unfortunately, we, the uncommitted members of the technological community, are saddened by such reactions by the clergy for two reasons. Firstly they are undoubtedly misguided and most surely unavailing; but above all they run contrary to our certainty that it *is* good to ameliorate the hardships of the cosmic plan whenever we can, both on our own behalf and on behalf of those less fortunate than ourselves. And how can we stifle our disappointment at the ill judgement of the clergy when we find them so very frequently doing this sort of thing? For example, consider their reaction to the invention of lightning conductors—surely, of all things, the most beneficent, agreeable, calm, silent and helpful among technological developments.

Franklin conceived the idea of the lightning rod when in 1752 he carried out his experiments with a kite on the banks of the Schuylkill River and showed that, provided the string was made to conduct, it would draw electric sparks from a thunder cloud. Unfortunately it had been part of the moral system of the clergy to aver that thunder was a noise produced by demons, the incarnation of badness, and that lightning was the

'. . . on theological grounds they condemned gas-lighting . . .'

sword of the Devil striking down a malefactor. Sometimes it was the Lord, the epitome of goodness, who was destroying a transgressor, but the principle was the same. We must remember that just about this period, in 1768, John Wesley in Protestant England was uttering his famous declaration in favour of witchcraft in which he thundered that 'the giving up of witchcraft is in effect the giving up of the Bible'. To ward off lightning, therefore, the only possible thing to do was to ring the consecrated bells, though holy relics and prayer might help a little too.

We must sadly recall that the advance of simple technology in the form of the protective lightning rod took place in spite of the clergy, and its adoption was made by them to be slow and halting when it might have been quick. Andrew White of Cornell wrote in 1895 how the

> Prince of the Power of the Air retreated before the light-ning-rod of Franklin . . . for his lightning-rod did what exorcisms, and holy water, and processions, and the *Agnus Dei*, and the ringing of church bells, and the rack, and the burning of witches, had failed to do. This was clearly seen, even by the poorest peasants in eastern France, when they observed that the grand spire of Strasburg Cathedral, which neither the sacredness of the place, nor the bells within it, nor the holy water and relics beneath it, could protect from frequent injuries by lightning, was once and for all protected by Franklin's rod.*

The step back was indeed reluctantly taken. A string of dates is available to historians for the number of occasions when the tower of St Mark's in Venice, even though sur-mounted by an angel and by bells, has been struck by light-ning. The list begins in 1388 and carries on through 1417, 1489, 1548, 1563, 1653 and 1745. To read in modern times of the damage, fire and loss of life is to experience incredulous

* From *A History of the Warfare of Science with Theology in Christendom* (Arco, 1955.)

surprise; we who live as naturally in a technological age as a fish swims in water have forgotten that such things happened. In 1752 the solution to the problem was provided for the asking. But it was not accepted. The church was badly struck in 1761 and again in 1762. Only in 1766 was a lightning rod installed —and the building has never been struck since.

We may feel that 1766 was a long time back, and that there was no need then for much effort to harmonise the application of science with the ordinary affairs of life. But it is sorrowful to tell that things were no better a hundred years later. Consider a machine that was clearly, had men had eyes to see, a forerunner of the many that now in our time have revolutionised agriculture and extinguished the peasantry as a social class. I refer to the introduction, at the beginning of the nineteenth century, of the mechanical winnowing machine for cleaning grain. This, and all the other machines, have changed rural living so that the country folk are now most clearly and suddenly exposed to both the good things of science and the bad ones. What did the clergy have to say? In Scotland, sad to tell, the use of these machines for fanning oats and barley was widely and flatly denounced as contrary to the text, 'The wind bloweth whithersoever it listeth'. Reference was also adduced to the accepted thesis that Satan is 'Prince of the powers of the air' and that consequently the use of a fan, even as part of a device containing sieves and wheels and pulleys as well, could only be construed as making a treaty with the Devil. And so, here we find the clergy taking up another unhelpful tactical position from which a melancholy ecclesiastical withdrawal soon had to be made.

Railways, which among all the early advances in technology made an obvious impact and produced a palpable change, were introduced in 1825. No opposing resistance came from the English clergy at their advent, but it is perhaps worth recalling that an Archbishop in France declared their introduction into that country to be a sign of the divine displeasure of Heaven at the behaviour of the country innkeepers who, in spite of the

admonitions of the Church, had adopted the pernicious practice of serving meat to travellers on fast days. Now, said the
Archbishop, the Lord had put it into the inventors' heads to
invent steam locomotives and had, furthermore, arranged for
capital to allow engineers to build railways all over France—
this somewhat elaborate manœuvre being carried out entirely
for the purpose of punishing the innkeepers who would for the
future see their previous sacrilegious customers whirled by at
speeds up to thirty miles an hour!

The clergy's business is with the spirit, and our need for their
help is most urgent when our minds and bodies are afflicted by
disease. In the new world of applied science we need them also,
but in another way. The dawning of the age of technology has
seen a gradual beating back of the tide of plague, infection and
pain as one pestilence after another has yielded to the advance
of science applied to medicine. We could have hoped that the
clergy would have been on hand to advise and guide us on how
best to use the new spans of life now freed for living. But it has
not happened like this.

The idea of preventing smallpox by inoculation seems to
have been suggested by Boyer in France early in the eighteenth
century, but it was also tried in England. Immediately the
clergy reacted, but unhelpfully. The theologians of the Sor-
bonne solemnly condemned it. The English clergy thundered
against it in such sermons as 'The Dangerous and Sinful
Practice of Inoculation' and 'Inoculation an Indefensible
Practice', and in 1753 it was denounced from the pulpit in
Canterbury. While a large body of ministers in Scotland
arraigned the practice as 'endeavouring to baffle a Divine
judgement', Dr Zabdiel Boylston of Boston, Mass., who in-
oculated his own son in 1721, was violently attacked and told
by the clergy that smallpox is 'a judgement of God on the sins
of the people and . . . to avert it is but to provoke Him more.'

Because the technological success of vaccination, the efficiency of which to ward off smallpox was reported by Jenner
in 1798, has been so obvious and striking, its impact on men's

minds and on the way they look on life has been proportionally dramatic and forceful. Instead of having to die, great numbers of people could now live to fulfil their purpose—which was ... what? To increase the export of cotton goods to Asia? Or for some better, non-economic purpose?

The unfortunate clergy, or at least the more enthusiastic brethren, tangle themselves in theological entrenchments from which they must eventually go, having helped nobody. The Anti-vaccination Society of 1798 seemed a good, firm redoubt; more sermons—'the law of God prohibits the practice'; Dr Ramsden at Cambridge in 1803 mingling scholarship, theology and abuse of Jenner—all were used as defences that crumbled as the smallpox deaths dwindled in Berlin, in Württemberg, in Copenhagen, in Vienna. ... And then the last tragic withdrawal in Montreal in the smallpox epidemic of 1885; this, mark you, within living memory!

The story is told by Andrew White.

In that year the smallpox broke with great virulence in Montreal. The Protestant population escaped almost entirely by vaccination; but multitudes of their Catholic fellow-citizens, under some vague survival of orthodox ideas, refused vaccination and suffered fearfully. When at last the plague became so serious that travel and trade fell off greatly and quarantine began to be established in neighbouring cities, an effort was made to enforce compulsory vaccination. The result was that large numbers ... resisted and even threatened bloodshed. The clergy at first tolerated and even encouraged this conduct: the Abbé Filiatrault ... declared in a sermon, 'If we are afflicted with smallpox it is because we had a carnival last winter feasting the flesh, which has offended the Lord ... it is to punish our pride that God has sent us smallpox.' The Board of Health ... addressed a circular to the . . . clergy imploring them to recommend vaccination; but though two or three complied with this request, the great majority were either silent or openly hostile . . . the faithful were exhorted to rely on devotional exercises of various sorts. . . . Meanwhile, the disease which had nearly died out among the Protestants, raged with ever-increasing virulence among the Catholics; and, the truth becoming more and more clear, even to the most devout, proper measures were at last enforced and the plague was stayed, though not until there had been a fearful waste of life.' *

The purpose of technological society is to produce goods as effortlessly as may be. The citizens of this society who are less than happy with this social purpose can never conceive themselves actively desiring to die or to be in pain as a substitute for the accepted enjoyment of the production of wealth. If they should turn to the clergy for help in defining a better purpose for life, they would expect this to be achieved in a tolerably healthy and pain-free environment.

This expectation might not be realised. Consider the reaction in Protestant Scotland to James Young Simpson's use of chloroform as an anaesthetic in childbirth in 1847. Never was there such a potent blast from the pulpits of Edinburgh. The use of chloroform was denounced as impious and contrary to Holy Writ. The clergy almost to a man (there were some exceptions) spoke warmly in favour of the moral worth of women continuing to suffer the pains which men would never share, and had, they asserted, good theological grounds for not wishing to see ameliorated.

But in due course, reluctantly and without comment or retraction, the clergy are compelled to withdraw. And the sight of their grudging progress backwards, step by step, is melancholy to citizens of the technological society of today who need their advice.

The use of anaesthetics as a modern means of improving the practice of surgery and obstetrics and protecting patients against pain strikes the normal mind as admirable. Yet the

* *Op. cit.*

scientific insight that enables modern research to evolve new chemical compounds and that at the same time allows the physiologist to achieve improved control over the operation of the brain does raise points where a comment on purpose from a non-committed person could usefully show the way. We are at last all agreed, technological citizens and clergy alike, that the quelling of physical pain by the use of anaesthetics is something that should obviously be done. But what of mental distress? The business executive, worried and frustrated by the problems of maintaining a rising output of refrigerators, can fortify himself against the strain of his next conference by taking a tranquilliser pill! Is this a good idea? Provided that he does not irrevocably damage his nervous system, why should he not take advantage of what technology has to offer, and live most of his working life under the influence of tranquillisers?

When in 1847 Simpson was fighting the clergy for the use of chloroform in childbirth, he struck a decisive blow in the battle when he thought solemnly to quote Genesis 2, 21, and claimed that in it anaesthetics were approved—particularly midwifery—since Jehovah, before he took the rib from Adam's side for the creation of Eve, caused a deep sleep to fall upon him. Today the clergy cling less rigidly to their written text and are less ready to attribute earthquakes and disease as punishment for moral turpitude and general bad behaviour. The uncommitted citizen, however, can hope that the clergy have not stepped back so far that they will not be on hand to help solve the problem of the ethical position of the man who —while working hard and producing efficiency —is living in an imaginary world produced by tranquillisers and mescaline.

The nonconformist members of modern societies do not find it a sufficient purpose for living merely to produce economic wealth. Their views are best expressed in the words attributed by Rupert Brooke to another species:

> Fish say, they have their Stream and Pond;
> But is there anything Beyond?

Backwards with the Clergy

This life cannot be All, they swear,
For how unpleasant, if it were!

And the clergy too, while stepping backwards and relaxing
their grip on those parts of their views that in the past caused
them to abjure lightning rods, grain-winnowing machines and
chloroform, have still to give a clear picture of the nature and
purpose of man to those who seek an alternative to that offered
by applied science.

And what kind of a decision can be said to have been reached
about man and the animals? So far as animals are concerned,
Mount Ararat has for a very long time been a great trouble to
the clergy. Even in the early days of the Christian era, St
Augustine was worried on the 'question about all these kinds
of beasts, which are neither tamed by man, nor spring from the
earth like frogs, such as wolves and others of that sort ... as to
how they could find their way to the islands after that flood
which destroyed every living thing not preserved in the ark.'
And Joseph Acosta in 1590 very reasonably points out the
difficulties, not only of Noah's housing all the diverse beasts
but in the creatures distributing themselves so widely afterwards. 'Who can imagine', he asks, 'that in so long a voyage
men woulde take the paines to carrie Foxes to Peru, especially
that kinde they call "Acias", which is the filthiest I have seene?
Who woulde likewise say that they have carried Tygers and
Lyons? Truly it were a thing worthy the laughing at to thinke
so.'

But it remained in truth no laughing matter, and many men
struggled to explain how the ark could possibly have been big
enough to contain all the species of animals that were being
found to inhabit the earth and how Adam could possibly have
found time to make up names for all of them. Right to the end
of the eighteenth century it was necessary orthodox dogma to
believe that every species of creatures on earth was fixed in its
class and that man was fixed too—a different and superior
animal for whom all the rest of creation had been made.

The technological age in which we now live had its beginnings in the steam engine of the eighteenth century; it grew up with the machines and the coal-tar dyes of the nineteenth century; and is flowering with the present control of the natural environment that we enjoy today. But the change in ourselves and the beginnings of our willingness to submit ourselves wholeheartedly to the doctrine of applied science can be argued to have started on 1 July 1858. Because on that date we realised that we were not the kind of animal we had thought we were and—it is not, I hope, too harsh to say—the clergy failed to provide any advice on the direction we ought to have taken, it being then seen what kind of animal we were.

On 1 July 1858 Charles Darwin presented to the Linnaean Society Alfred Wallace's memorandum together with his own comments, and thus set out the facts upon which is based the understanding that animal species—and ourselves, that is, man as well—are not immutable creations, but are all linked one to another by the process of biological evolution.

Bishop Wilberforce's attack on Huxley at the meeting of the British Association in 1861, when he asked him whether he was descended from a monkey on his father's or his mother's side, is worth remembering by us modern citizens because the force of Huxley's reply struck the clergy a blow from which they never recovered. And their damaged confidence has been our loss today. Huxley said that he would rather be allied to an ape than to a bishop misrepresenting the truth. But Wilberforce sincerely believed that 'the principle of natural selection is absolutely incompatible with the word of God'. Cardinal Manning described it as a 'brutal philosophy—to wit, there is no God, and the ape is our Adam'. Monseigneur Ségur in France wrote, 'These infamous doctrines have for their only support the most abject passions. Their father is pride, their mother impurity, their offspring revolutions. They came from hell and return thither, taking with them the gross creatures who blush not to proclaim and accept them.' Dr Perry, Bishop of Melbourne, in a bitter book called *Science and the Bible* declared that the object of Darwin and Huxley was to 'produce in their readers a disbelief in the Bible'.

This indeed has been the problem of living in the present world of science and technology. In the early days of the Church there were the most violent and murderous contests between those who interpreted Holy Writ one way and those who interpreted it another. Platoons of bishops encouraged their followers to slaughter and destroy in order to maintain that one member of the Trinity was superior to another or to support some detail of the interpretation of the mystery of the incarnation. Opposing companies of bishops with their adherents marched out to do equal violence in support of an opposite metaphysical belief. The word as written has been interpreted in different ways and with devastating sincerity and conviction. The Nestorians tried their hardest to exterminate the Monophysites—all in the cause of the good life. But this was a matter of opinion, of faith. St Simon Stylites considered that it was of assistance in living the good life to be dirty; and so filthy was his condition and so intolerable his smell that visitors could not bear to come near him. On the other hand the inspired utterance is attributed to John Wesley that 'cleanliness is near akin to godliness'.

These are matters of belief. The new problem posed by science was how to co-ordinate these views with those con- clusions derived from the sort of material evidence with which science deals. And faced with this, ideas—whether of laymen or clergy—as to man's purpose have changed so completely that the trial of Thomas Scopes in Dayton, Tennessee, accused of the crime of teaching the principles of biological evolution, seemed to most people an anachronistic survival from an earlier age when it took place in the year 1925.

The refugee from technology, who for some reason has not been caught up in the urge to produce more efficiently and con- sume more conspicuously, will not be altogether disappointed to find that the clergy have been stepping backwards, even though they may seem less helpful to him than he hoped they would be. At least in their backward progression in face of the forward march of science they have abandoned the monstrous pursuit and torture of wretched old women accused of witchcraft. Pope Eugene IV in 1437 issued a bull exhorting the inquisitors to use greater diligence against witches, expecially those who had the power to produce bad weather. Pope Innocent VIII, inspired by the scriptural command, 'Thou shalt not suffer a witch to live', exhorted the clergy of Germany to find out, by every extreme of torture if need be, those who by occult means were destroying vineyards, gardens, meadows and growing crops. At least the modern sciences of meteorology and plant pathology have given us cause to be thankful for an improvement over these most dreadful examples of bad behaviour—carried out, let it be said, for the most highminded of motives. Yet as late as 1773, the Associated Presbytery of Protestant Scotland continued to reaffirm their belief in witchcraft. However, besides retreating eventually from their positive assertions about witches, the clergy have relaxed their opposition to lightning rods and anaesthetics and vaccination and the evidence derived from the science of geology about the age of the earth. With their acceptance of Darwin's evidence that man has evolved from lower animals, comes some measure of fusion of ideas with those scientists, the citizens of the Technological Society, who have been arguing that the way men ought to behave can be deduced by reasoning from the way mankind has evolved.

While the big battalions of scientists and the lay citizens who march with them have accepted wholeheartedly and without question the thesis that the purpose of existence is a rich supply of material objects and a life comprising a fractional working week in an automated factory, free from disease, hardship or worry and fully provided with piped-in entertainment, there have been a few others who have bent their minds to the problem of whether science, that has so ruthlessly pressed the clergy backwards, can itself provide a code of behaviour better than that accepted by those who conform so readily as men-of-the-modern-world.

The main line of thought of those who have considered how science can guide the behaviour of men in a technological society has taken as a starting point the newer understanding of the scope of evolution. Julian Huxley has summarised this current understanding in three sections. First comes cosmological evolution wherein, through a period of about 5000 million years, was formed the galaxy of the Milky Way in which the Sun is a minor star. Attached to the Sun is a minor planet, namely, the earth—and on it us. The next phase is biological evolution. The earth's climate becomes such that biological life can start and, once started, in 2000 million years or so the simple living creatures evolve to the number and complexity we now see; hence the eyes of the falcon, the wings of the hover-fly and the mechanism developed by orchids to ensure cross-pollination—with ourselves as the most complex biological structure of all.

The third stage of evolution, according to this classification, is the one in which we are now living. Huxley calls it the 'psychosocial phase' and it has not lasted for even one million years; indeed this part of the evolutionary process to which we attach such personal importance has only been in operation for about 10,000 years. It warrants special attention, says Huxley, because for the first time in biological history an animal—man—has itself willed and achieved evolutionary changes by taking thought. For example, before bats were able to fly, generations of them had to live and die with only inadequate membranes between their fingers, until by chance a few families luckily born with more ample webbing survived better in the cruel competitive world and took their place as a separate species where the ability to fly improved their ability to survive. Man can now fly, but he did not need to wait until a family of flying men happened to be born. By using his brains he thought up an aeroplane just as he had already thought of warm clothes, and fires, and agriculture.

The Science Myth

The biological scientist sees the changes that have taken place since people scrambled about like Australian aborigines or jungle pigmies, until today many of us drive smooth cars, read books, fly, play bridge and go to the theatre or to church as evidence of 'psychosocial' evolution. The backward march of the clergy and the forward march of the scientist are parts of the same process too. Reviewing the progress of this 'psycho-social phase' as a whole some scientists feel that they can identify the purpose of Technological Society. Julian Huxley calls it the fulfilment of the evolutionary process on this earth.

It is very clever of scientists to be able to make their countries wealthy and it is understandable of the Americans to try to train more technologists in order to produce more television sets and nuclear reactors than the Russians. It is equally understandable of the British and the French and the Swedes and the Germans, the Mexicans and the Japanese, all to press forward at maximum speed to outstrip each other. But for those who doubt the virtues of submitting to technology and who, at the same time, find that the clergy have explained away almost all their traditional written rules without substituting any more satisfactory and up-to-date precepts in their place, it is perhaps a little disappointing to find that the best theological principle produced by science itself is that 'man's most sacred duty ... is to promote the maximum fulfilment of the evolutionary process.'

If the refugee citizen of the Technological Society in search of a purpose finds this rationalist creed a little lacking in warmth he can pursue other systems of good manners also built on scientific logic. Professor C. H. Waddington, a distinguished embryologist, has recently developed at some length a system of scientific ethics. In brief, he reasons that things of good repute, nobility, truth, justice, courage, kindness—all these are virtues because they possess biological advantages as social behaviour. Man has evolved as a social animal who lives in an organised group the effectiveness of which, just like that of a pack of wolves, a shoal of fish, a flock of starlings, or a herd of deer, depends on the social acceptability of each of its members. When a herd of deer is feeding, one will act as a sentinel; and it is the faithfulness, diligence and self-sacrifice of this one individual that protects all the rest from being eaten by lions.

Good. The refugee Technologist can be pleased. The ethics of deer apply very well to men. But we cannot stop yet. Good social behaviour, for deer or men, requires what the biologists call 'role differentiation'; one deer watches while the others eat. This separation of function, however, is itself derived from a situation in which an older deer teaches a younger deer its duties as a sentry. In this society, therefore, there must be someone who has authority and someone else who accepts authority. Biological scientists, with their weakness for abstract principles, have called these two parts of the social organisation the 'authority-bearing' and the 'authority-accepting' entities.

The scientific argument that now develops is that the ethical system to which man conforms, based though it may be at the start on social behaviour that gives the clan an improved chance of survival in the evolutionary struggle for existence, soon comes to be transmitted by the teaching of those in authority—whether they be mothers, grandmothers, chieftains or the clergy—and by deference to this teaching in those who are prepared to accept authority. And scientific observations are soon able to throw a great deal of light on the reasons why at a certain age people are readily prepared to embrace as unquestionable truth what they are taught.

The Austrian biologist, Konrad Lorenz, has described a peculiar process of authority-acceptance in ducks and geese. If a newly-hatched duckling meets under appropriate circumstances a moving creature other than its mother, it attaches its allegiance to it, whether it be a dog, a clockwork toy, or a man, and thereafter will follow it about and transfer to it its devotion. The well-known case of Mary's little lamb is another example of this sort of thing.

But the biological scientists have gone deeper into the mechanisms by which individuals give their loyalty and obedience to those whom they accept as being 'authority-bearing' and from whom they acquire their ideas of good behaviour and of right and wrong. Professor Harlow, of the University of Wisconsin, has made a study of infant monkeys. These were taken away from the society of all other monkeys, including their mothers, a few hours after birth and were put alone into a warm laboratory. The following experiment was then done. Two dummy 'mother' monkeys were put into the laboratory with the baby monkey. Both of these had the same kind of dummy head and each of them had the teat of a feeding. bottle protruding from 'her' breast, but whereas the body of one of these effigies was made of wire, the other was covered with soft, cosy, Terry-towelling. The important discovery was made that it did not make any difference to the physical well-being of the baby monkeys whether they received their milk from the wire 'mother' or the Terry-towelling 'mother'. On the other hand, all the monkeys turned to the Terry-towel 'mother' and the Terry-towel 'mother' alone, whether it gave milk or not, whenever they needed comfort or reassurance. Little monkeys that were confronted by the alarming presence of a mechanical teddy-bear beating a drum were terrified— unless they had a Terry-towel mother to turn to, when they quickly overcame their terror and soon became quite disrespectful to the previously terrifying bogy.

Waddington implies that just as the monkeys developed emotional love and dependence for dummy mothers—provided that they were of the appropriate consistency—and accepted them as 'authority-bearing' entities, so in like manner the young of the human species may absorb their first ideas about authority and ethics and the way to behave from their mothers, largely on the basis of their shape and consistency. This argument could, of course, be extended further in child-rearing. If the scientific community decided to dispense with the real mother and substitute an appropriately constructed dummy, the ethical system implanted in the child's mind by his first 'authority-bearing' entity with which the young citizen came into contact might be different from what it would otherwise have been.

The scientific doctrine to which society has almost accidentally found itself having to conform is primarily concerned with material wealth and well-being. The countryside is to be built over with nuclear power stations and super-highways and modern 'homes' because such wealth is what comes out of technology. The ethical systems of the clergy, whether they be austerity, poverty and celibacy, death for the Faith on the spears of the infidels, or more subtle virtues such as truthfulness and clear thinking and kindliness, tend to get tarnished and trampled down in the technological bustle of the rising standard of living. The metaphysical dogma is in any event progressively lost as scientific knowledge increases. In this field, revelation is no match for patient research, and Franklin's rod will always beat the ringing of consecrated bells when it comes to protecting church towers against lightning. Nevertheless, the more thoughtful citizens feel sad when they watch the teachings of the clergy being eroded away.

Can scientific logic itself not fill the vacuum? Only a few brave men claim that it can. It takes a very special kind of person to be able to strive and suffer and be kind to his aged relatives out of a belief that he is promoting 'the fulfilment of the evolutionary process on this earth'. And there is one very unsatisfactory feature about the hypothesis that ethical systems are a development of biological evolution. The evidence from the science of biology showing the appearance of 'authority-accepting' entities at a certain stage in evolution is convincing and we can also turn to the patient work of the psychologists showing the building up of a 'super-ego' which, like Hamlet's father's ghost, follows us about and tells us how we ought to behave. But can we really be sure that the scientific approach will not prove even less helpful to the Technological Refugee than continued dependence on the retreating clergy?

We can quite readily accept the hypothesis that ethical systems are a part of our evolutionary progress as biological entities and that we must expect them to develop and change as we gallop forward through the present age of 'psychosocial evolution'. But although we may allow that the forces of evolution are capable of producing an ethical system for us, the individualists making up the small groups of people who worry about the matter are not quite sure whether they are going to like the kind of ethical system that emerges. Dr A. Booth recently referred to an incident in which a Soviet electronic computer designed to translate English into Russian dealt with the phrase 'out of sight, out of mind'. As it happened, an American computer geared to translate Russian into English picked up the Russian translation and rendered it back again as 'invisible lunatic'. Perhaps the ethical systems evolved will support the exposing of infants on mountainsides, the extermination of the Jews, or the abandonment of the notion that anything is superior to anything else.

Philosophers have been considering man and the good life for several thousand years. Our own civilisation was based on the classical tradition invented by the Greeks in the brief period round about 450 B.C. We have enjoyed the splendid ethics of Christianity running through the varied vicissitudes of changing metaphysics—the Nestorian Dogma, the Monophysites, devotees of witchcraft, original sin, fundamentalists, Puritans, 'Wee Frees'—and now the scientific approach to truth has begun to generate a metaphysic of its own. Gibbon, reviewing fifteen hundred years of the history of the West, confidently asserts, 'If a man were called to fix a period in the history of the world during which the condition of the human race was most happy and prosperous, he would without hesitation name that which elapsed from the death of Domitian to the accession of Commodus.' This was from the year 96 to the year 180. The Romans of this period may have had their faults but they also possessed great virtues. They accepted the teaching of the clergy of all creeds with toleration. The Gods of Rome and of foreigners were equally welcome if they could help a man to virtue. Prominent citizens took their part in religious services as a civic duty. The Romans were businesslike and efficient and, like ourselves, applied their technological abilities to the affairs of the community. But perhaps the most important lesson for us now was the fact that they had in their minds a practical ethic of the way in which it was noble and civilised for a Roman to behave.

7

BREAKFAST IN BED

CONFORMITY to the rigidity of the times is required of people even when they are ill in bed. A hundred and fifty years ago, a sick man was conditioned to accept as beneficial the automatic reaction of his physician, which was to draw six ounces of blood. Fifty years ago, at the height of the Industrial Revolution and at the time when science and technology were taking their places as the guiding principles of behaviour, the administration of castor oil was accepted as a beneficial treatment for a wide variety of ills ranging from measles to gout. Even today comparatively thoughtful people accept as a matter of axiomatic truth the virtues of laxatives. Indeed, prosperous businesses, many of them models of scientific organisation, are based on a brisk and continuing consumption of laxative drugs by intelligent members of the community.

Other pressures bear on the citizen to ensure that he shall fit the accepted mould even in the privacy of his meals. Famine and starvation have haunted mankind since the beginning of history and continue to this day as real and imminent danger for the majority of the world's population. And besides hunger and starvation, there are to be found among the less fortunate nations of the earth great numbers of people suffering, not from famine, but from diseases due to the consumption of inadequate diets that fail to provide one or other of the diverse components that a man—or a child—must have to be properly fed. Deprived children whose only food is cereal gruel waste and die from protein-malnutrition, often called 'kwashiorkor', even in the 1960s when the technological societies prosper so ostentatiously. There are people who sicken and die from beri-beri because almost the only food they are able to obtain is white rice. Corn-meal mush, molasses and little else have been known for thirty years to lead to pellagra, a disease with three main end-results: dermatitis, diarrhoea and dementia. And pellagra can still be found.

These and other ills have been pinned down by scientific evidence to shortcomings in the composition of the meals that people eat. This knowledge, like that of lightning rods and chloroform and automation and the building of great factories to take advantage of scientific and technological achievements —and the development of intricate organisations to run them —has been productive of much good. But at the same time there has been a price to pay. Part of the price becomes due if the scientific knowledge applied to the national food is not, in fact, complete. It has been hinted that a nation's babies may consume too much vitamin D if the 'protective' additions to their national dried milk are unintentionally raised too high. There is also some debate as to whether the calorie intake of a nation may not, even under the most expert and pervasive scientific guidance, be increased to such a level that the happy period of childhood shrinks while the children grow faster and faster and married life begins before they leave school. But the main problem arising from the application of science to diet is the same as that springing from its application to other aspects of life: it has tended to demand uniformity.

The bakery of modern times is a factory containing a complex of largely automatic machinery. The flour is sucked into great storage hoppers, its composition standardised by chemical and physical tests and adjusted by the appropriate addition of 'improvers' and 'additives'. It is metered into mixers, converted into dough and leavened under conditions as fully controlled by electronic instruments as a plastics factory. For those whose curiosity is aroused, this process of leavening is of some philosophical significance. It is achieved by the living creature, *Saccharomyces cerevisiae*—yeast. It is interesting to note, that now that the horse and the donkey have almost disappeared as domestic animals, the ox is no longer put to the plough, the dog team displaced by the snow-tractor in the Arctic, and even the elephant abandoned to make room for the internal combustion engine in the teak forests of Burma, yeast remains as the last living creature used by man for the development of power. The function of yeast in dough is to pull out and stretch the elastic fibres of gluten so that the loaf, when it is eventually formed, shall possess its desirable tense silky structure.

The yeast that does this is grown in a yeast factory. Its breeding is as carefully controlled as once was that of a shire horse. The technologists in charge of the yeast population put their brood mares to stud exactly like horse breeders, except that they manipulate their stock with fine glass needles on a microscope slide. The selected strain is then grown up with every attention to its nourishment, its warmth and comfort, and its freedom from infection. The object of the people who grow yeast is that, so far as is possible, each individual that makes up the mass shall be as like its neighbour as possible. This is, of course, so that later on in the dough their pull shall be uniform throughout. Nevertheless, just as happens with a bunch of cattle or a string of horses from the same parents, the separate members of the family possess their own individuality. Yet so successful in their efforts are the people who organise the growth of the huge population of yeast required to raise the dough that the travelling ovens in which the final stage of the yeast's life and work take place can be run at an exactly controlled and uniform speed, and when the yeast has at last succumbed to the heat all the loaves, as they come out of the oven, rank after rank on the moving platform, are as closely similar as could be wished. The living yeasts are simple creatures, yet the uniformity in performance imposed on them by the producers of yeast represents, in its way, a remarkable standardisation of life brought about by technical means.

For the citizen of an industrial state, much of the food he eats must be standardised. Besides bread, cakes as well will need to be produced automatically. There is, for example, a factory in London in which standardised Swiss roll—very good Swiss roll, mark you, but standardised—is produced continuously by a remarkable machine by the mile. Animal foods are also produced to standard specifications. Hens, all belonging to the same family, kept in rows of cages in a battery and fed on the identical ration will, as might be expected, lay eggs of uniform size, colour and flavour. Wholesale purveyors of meat to be processed into standard cellophane-wrapped portions for sale at fixed prices in super-markets require a uniform raw material to start with. This is produced by farmers who choose an appropriate breed of animal and appropriately balanced rations. The farmers are now also possessed of the scientific knowledge that allows them to grow the legs of the animals longer or shorter and the loins fatter or leaner. Dr John Hammond of Cambridge University has published detailed scientific evidence showing that if a lamb or a calf is fed large amounts of food when it is young and less when it is a little older, its body configuration—and the portions supplied to the super-market—will be different than they would be if the animal were fed less when it was young and more later. Further differences in shape take place if the feeding is ample both when the beast is young and as it grows older.

The conditions under which human beings are conscribed are not so rigorous or so wholeheartedly imposed as are those to which pigs, sheep and cattle are compelled to submit, yet there is a certain similarity. We have already discussed the way in which the large-scale methods of modern food industry make it inevitable that there should be a high degree of uniformity in the main articles of diet available to the members of a Technical Community. In the eighteenth century, a noble-man going on the grand tour of Europe could have his carriage made to suit his individual whim. He could have his tea sent from Soochong, his bread baked extra crusty and his preserved strawberries from his housekeeper's still-room. Procrustes decrees today that a twentieth-century gentleman's motorcar is a standard model like everyone else's and his tea, bread and jam the branded products of their respective manufacturers.

And even should he send out for a bunch of roses for his drawing room, they too will be uniform, standard blooms as even, one with the other, as if they had been turned on a lathe to a single standard specification.

Uniformity and standardisation are essential attributes of the manufactured foods of Technological Society. Recognition of this important fact transformed Mr Thomas Lipton, the first man to pre-pack a uniform blend of tea, from a struggling Glasgow grocer into a titled yachtsman. Today, dependable branded articles of food represent a triumph for the scientists and technologists who ensure the uniformity of their colours and tastes and consistencies, who determine their freedom from chemical and bacteriological contamination, and who achieve wonders in packaging and storage.

Fish provide interesting examples of the way in which the rigidities of modern times and the continuous advance of applied science compel people to conform. Part of the conformity is good, but part—and the subtle compulsion itself— is bad.

Almost up to the present time fish available in a modern industrial community is not a particularly outstanding testimony to the technical and scientific skills which had been applied to its organisation and treatment. And fish themselves are still an anomaly in the modern world by being the sole remaining wild animals used by civilised man as a major foodstuff. All other foods, animal and vegetable alike, have been domesticated. Fish alone fend for themselves, going and coming without benefit of farm, pasture of fertilizer. And, like the bison before them, they are hunted down by anyone who can locate where they roam. Perhaps they may in due time share the bison's fate and be exterminated; the danger certainly exists.

A considerable amount of scientific effort has been applied to the catching of fish. Powerful and well-equipped ships scour the seas. Some go a three week's voyage or more into the Arctic seas to catch their prey. Modern radar equipment is used to locate

'... *Uniformity and standardisation are essential attributes* ...'

the shoals, and carefully designed nets are used to catch the different types of fish desired. Yet in spite of the amount of capital invested in the operation and the technical ability devoted to catching fish, the individualistic behaviour required in facing the storms and vagaries of the ocean has spilled over into the marketing of the product. Thus it has happened that for a long while fish as a commodity has been a glaring exception from the accepted notion that commodities should be suited to the modern scene. It is true that by going to the fish quay at dawn, a hotel keeper would sometimes buy a halibut of exquisite quality or could select something to suit the taste of a customer of particular discrimination. But fish lacked the essential feature required by the present-day complex, crowded world. They did not measure up to a standard specification and —to speak plainly—many of them were downright bad. Year by year the amount of 'prime' table fish on the market has tended to dwindle and the average quality of the total catch to become poorer.

Fish, therefore, was an anachronism in the present age of applied science. It was inappropriate that a few individualistic epicures were able, by taking trouble, to obtain now and then a special article of special quality—a really fresh sole, whiting with their tails in their mouths, red mullet. The trend of the times is that standard articles of good, but not outrageously good, quality should be available throughout the year and without trouble from a widespread net of suppliers. These standard commodities are today's 'foods of convenience'. Fish have outstandingly been foods of inconvenience.

Now all this is changing. As the sale of so-called fresh fish continues to dwindle, standardised packs are replacing the non-standard, boney individual fishes, some of which were of dubious quality, previously to be seen on the fishmongers' slabs. Frozen fish fillets and branded 'fish fingers' are doing for the fish trade what packaged tea did earlier for the tea trade. Technological advances in quick freezing are at last allowing the producers to market a uniform standard article. Fish has been converted into a 'food of convenience'. The rank-and-file citizen is the gainer and only the nonconformist is the loser. While he shares with his fellows the life of the industrial community in a town, where his house is small and his wife is engaged in industry too, the pressure of the times impels him to eat, not the fruits of the sea, but what the food industry manufactures.

The pressure exerted on a citizen of an industrialised country to eat a standardised diet made up of uniform packaged articles brings its force to bear in a subtle way. Consider cornflakes. In less highly organised times before applied science had acquired the pervasive strength it possesses today, cornflakes had not been invented and people ate all sorts of different things for breakfast. Then in 1898, cornflakes were brought into existence by Dr John Kellogg as part of the confused and quasi-religious activities of the Seventh Day Adventists. They were claimed to be something quite special—health foods, in fact. The idea of moral virtue arising from right eating was very much in the air and a number of similar foods were launched at about the same time. Dr Kellogg himself started the Sanitas Nut Food Company to market Protose, claimed to be the nutritional equivalent of beef steak, and Nuttose, allegedly equal in value to veal. Carson, in his book *The Cornflake Crusade*, has described the confused historical events: how in 1903, C. W. Post disseminated the virtues of Grape Nuts and Postum and asserted that 'you can recover from any ordinary disease by discontinuing coffee and poor food and using Postum Food Coffee and Grape Nuts'.

The strong beliefs about health and virtue have passed but packaged breakfast foods remain. Indeed, archaeologists of the future disinterring details of the habits and customs of the present age will agree that one of the most rigid rules of behaviour of twentieth-century industrial peoples was the regular consumption each morning of this uniform standardised product. Carson himself, who has taken for his historical study this particular incident in industrial progress, has pointed out that, regardless of the peculiar circumstances of their birth, packaged breakfast cereals possessed a fitness which made their advent inevitable. They added variety and flavour to the diet, they were fresh and clean,. they were storable, and, above all, they possessed the valuable advantage in the restless hurry of industrial life—they could be eaten straight from the box.

Music and painting, the ballet and poetry, these are expressions of man's spirit that have a place quite apart from his struggles at work. Indeed, for some people the hardships of their employment are repaid by the pleasures of these arts which rank for them as the most precious sweets of their hours of unemployment. And to music, dancing, pictures and literature the French would add the delights of the dining table. The trend of the times, however, does not encourage the fulfilment of this notion.

At one time cheese could be considered a delicacy not too far different from wine. Cheeses made in different parts of the country possessed their special aromas, just as wines vary with the soils on which the grapes are grown. Some seasons produced better flavoured cheeses than others. With the coming of applied science, this attitude towards cheese changed. To the nutritionist, it was a vehicle for first-class animal protein, calcium and certain valuable vitamins. To the chemist, the manufacture of cheese consisted in the coagulation of the protein, the adsorption upon it of much of the milk calcium and the removal of the aqueous fraction; it is, therefore, a convenient method of concentrating and preserving milk nutrients. And with the coming age of industrial productivity it became important for cheese, as marketed, to be a uniform article like a packet of cigarettes or a branded tin of 'instant' coffee.

The virtual disappearance of interesting local cheeses is only due in part to the pressure for uniformity. The progress of science in agriculture has been just as potent a factor in their extinction. In Great Britain, for example, cheese production has been steadily falling during most of the present century due

largely to modern developments in the production and distribution of liquid milk. The introduction of a stable and increasing all-the-year-round market for milk and the use of the
cow as a valuable industrial investment that can only be
profitably exploited if it is used as a producing unit throughout
the season has undermined cheese-making traditions. In the
days when cows were allowed to calve 'naturally' in the spring,
just when the first grass was coming along, there was a seasonal
flush of milk much of which would have gone to waste if it had
not been turned into cheese on the farm. In the winter the
cheese-making dairy farms went into hibernation.

Modern nutritional science calls for a steady production of
liquid milk throughout the year so that schoolchildren and
adolescents, and workmen as well, may always be able to
obtain their nutritional needs, either by bringing in the bottle
or carton from their doorsteps in the morning, or from automatic refrigerated vending machines. And scientific animal
husbandry makes it possible for the up-to-date farmer to
organise the biological programme of his cows to meet the
required nutritional and economic programme. Hence, there
is no surplus milk available for the making of local cheeses on
local farms. Cheese, when it is made at all, is produced in a
large specialised cheese factory, in standardised form for the
mass market. This inevitably involves the virtual disappearance of the special variety enjoyed by the connoisseur and concentration on a brand acceptable to the 'lowest common
denominator' of the population, sometimes affectionately described as 'mouse-trap'. The last phase in the process is the disappearance altogether of individual cheese as such and the
manufacture of 'process' cheese. This is made by mincing up
cheeses and mixing them together into a standard blend. A
scientifically selected emulsifying agent may be added and perhaps a dye as well and the whole pasteurised. The pasteurisa-
tion will virtually stop any changes taking place—either beneficial changes of ripening or harmful changes of decay. The
mass can then safely be divided into segments, wrapped and

packed and marketed in a form to suit a technological community.

The complex crowded society of today undoubtedly imposes pressures on its members. And although it allows a remarkable diversity in the food they eat, because science makes it possible to bring meat and fruit and spices and more delicacies of all sorts half-way round the world and has, as well, done away with foods that are only available 'in season'—science has extinguished the season: strawberries are a commonplace in December, and we can safely eat oysters whether there is an R in the month or not—nevertheless because technological processing requires uniformity, people who depend on it must give up any predilection they may have had for the non-standard and conform to the carefully selected quality chosen for them.

The selection of what qualities shall be provided by mass industry, whether for food or for anything else, is a complex business. There is a peculiar ceremony that takes place each day in all well-conducted British prisons. The prison governor, accompanied by his chief officer, passes through the precincts of the gaol and enters the kitchen where the day's meals are set out for his inspection. He looks at the porridge, examines the cocoa, and the stew (or the fish, according to the day of the week), the suet duff, or the rice. He looks at the bread and perhaps pinches it. Then, unless something is remarkably amiss, he nods his approval and moves on. Uniformity has been maintained; the food is of the required quality.

Now I would not for a moment belittle the judgement of a prison governor. Indeed, some twenty years ago, I had the professional duty of assessing the quality of prison diets. The food was uniformly wholesome and nourishing and free from contamination and dangerous infection. But although the special conditions under which a community of men live in a prison were such that they could be made to conform to the prison diet—and benefit from it—few individuals outside prison would have used the same criteria in judging the food as did the prison governor. We judge food quality by three different standards: by its nutritional composition, its sanitary state, and—most important, perhaps—by our emotional reaction to it.

Almost all foods possess an emotional flavour over and above their more material attributes. Caviar has had a superior social significance for 400 years or more. Tripe, unlike caviar, belongs to the extreme left. Bread has engaged the emotions of men and women more heatedly than any other food, and people to this day grow angry if they feel that their bread is too white—or not white enough. Applied science can make firm progress in matters of nutritional composition or of freedom from infection. It is when the few men responsible for the manufacture of our staple foods—the men who run the great food factories —it is when these technical experts fix a quality to which everyone must conform, because there is nothing else to eat, that nonconformists may feel the pressures of the time burdensome.

But the uniformity imposed on our eating goes further than the insistence that each article shall always be the same. Pressure is also exerted to prevent undue variability in the pattern of diet as a whole. In a Western industrial community the pressure exerted on a man or woman to eat bacon and egg for breakfast may almost amount to compulsion. This compulsion may be reinforced by a backing of allegedly scientific reasoning. There have been learned papers published in scientific journals to prove that nutritional health and well-being depend on the consumption of a hot breakfast. It is implied that if such a hot meal is not eaten symptoms of malnutrition will intervene. In other not widely different communities the emphasis may be on the importance of orange juice in the morning for the adequate subsistence of the human species. But apart from the allegedly scientific significance of different types of food and different varieties of meals at selected times of the day, the customs in technological societies tend to be applied with great rigidity. The standardised food that we have previously discussed—the baked beans, the selected, foil-wrapped cuts of meat, the Swiss roll, the frozen vegetables, the sliced bread, the pasteurised packaged and tested milk—all these are designed to be eaten, and the pressure on consumers to eat them is very great. Furthermore, this pressure is maintained throughout the life of the people who live within its influence.

The type of pressure exerted in the United States, for example, is different from that exerted in, say, Great Britain, and that in Great Britain is different from the pressure in Japan or Finland. Dr John Hammond studied the waves of growth produced in a pig when it was fed on a high plane of nutrition during the early period of its life. This wave of nutrition tended to culminate in the loin. Similarly in human beings, where the plane of nutrition imposed in children is a high one and this high plane of nutrition is followed by another later in adolescence equally high, the configuration of the finished adult is of a characteristic shape that makes it possible to identify a United States-fed young lady from, let us say, an Italian or British-fed one even if she is only visible in silhouette.

The application of science and technology to food supply, processing and distribution in a modern society exerts a direct Procrustean effect on the members of that society. This effect is, quite literally, to stretch him. In 1912, when the application of technological methods to American society was in its early stages, the average height of the men between 30 and 35 who insured their lives, and who were consequently examined and, it seems, measured by insurance doctors, was 5 feet 7·6 inches. In 1955, an equivalent group of men also between 30 and 35 were measured by what, on the face of it, would seem to be an unexpected branch of the national scientific establishment, namely, the Department of Agriculture. It was then found that the average height of Americans of this age had become 5 feet 9·6 inches. And this stretching was the same for women. The pervasive change in the national diet, which was of course linked to the social change in habits and the increase in wealth due to the ever increasing application of technology, caused

the average American woman of 20 to 29 years old to increase
in length from 5 feet 2·4 inches in 1900–1908 to 5 feet 4·3 inches
in 1955.

The heights of men and women obviously depend on the
growth of the children they once were. One of the most
obvious and dramatic results of the advance in technology,
bringing as it does wealth, nutritional knowledge, and skill-
fully and knowledgeably processed and packaged foods, has
been the faster and faster growth of the children. This increase
in rate has also accompanied an increase in the ultimate size at
which growth has come to a stop. Year after year in Liverpool,
the records extending almost unbroken since 1911 have shown
that the 5-year-old, 8-year-old and 12-year-old schoolchildren
are each year taller than were their contemporaries the year
before.

The scientific control of the national nutritional status, the
technological quality of the canned and frozen and packaged
foodstuffs available on the market to the members of industrial
society, and the strong pressure on the consumers to eat what
everyone else eats in a pattern of meals that might, it would
seem, almost be laid down by law, so rigidly is it supported—
all these factors exert their influence on the bodies of the people
who are exposed to them within a single generation. Japanese
who live in Japan, where the modern pressures, though severe,
are not yet fully up to those felt in the fully advanced communities where industrial technology is the basic and primary
philosophy, are people of short stature. In Hawaii, the climate
while less extreme technologically than in the continental
United States is more 'advanced' than in Japan. And it can be
seen that within a generation the Japanese who have moved
from Japan to live in the nutritional and social environment of
Hawaii have become stretched and are taller than those who
stayed at home. If, on the other hand, they choose to establish
themselves among the shipyards and factories and orange
groves of California and embrace at least some of the dietary
rules by which United States citizens are encompassed, then

they will soon find themselves drawn out still further and standing head and shoulders above their grandfather when he comes on a visit from Japan.

This is good, is it not? A big, tall, healthy Japanese is better than a thin, short, undernourished one. How easy wisdom would be if one only had to choose between black and white! To use science to prevent infants growing up deformed with their legs bent with rickets is an obvious good. To adopt efficient technological methods of production to bring wealth to a community so that good houses and clothes and enough food are available to everyone is admirable. If by whole-heartedly accepting applied science we can get all these things, let us do so. But there is a danger.

Although very few citizens of countries enjoying advanced technology and the wealth that accompanies it die from beri-beri or pellagra, which are vitamin-deficiency diseases, and although tuberculosis, which is aggravated by poor living conditions and inadequate food, is a disease of diminishing importance in modern industrial societies where scientific knowledge is applied to the maintenance of social welfare, nevertheless all is not well in countries where cellophane-wrapped lamb chops and full-standard ice-cream are widely distributed articles of diet. Dr Ancel Keys, of the University of Minnesota, pointed out that the proportion of middle-aged men dying of heart disease was much higher in the wealthy United States than in other less technologically developed countries. The figures for 1957 showed that whereas in Japan 94 men between 45 and 64 years old died of coronary disease per 100,000, there were 188 Italians, 345 Englishmen, 487 Scotsmen and 582 citizens of the United States.

There is a great deal of quite strong evidence to show that it is the rich foods, the products of the technologically advanced food industry, combined with the pressures of customs and pre-1957 scientific dietetics, that eventually each year kill the 582 American middle-aged men per 100,000. When the Japanese stay at home and refrain from ice-cream and pie and pints of milk, their middle-aged men survive. When they move to Hawaii and grow taller, more die from heart disease. And when, stretched tallest of all, they take up their residence in the United States itself, the wealthy technical society takes its toll and their older men die as often from heart failure as do the other Americans among whom they live.

The application of science and technology to the problems of the production of food and the selection of diets has brought immense benefits. The use of scientific knowledge about vitamin A prevented in World War II the suffering experienced twenty-five years before when children lacking vitamin A were blinded by xerophthalmia. The British, attentive to the understanding that vitamin A deficiency would do harm, fed halibut-liver oil to their young airmen so that their eyes would not be affected by night-blindness. Their general population ate vitamin A in their margarine and gained some from boiled greens. It is often, however, a principle of technological philosophy to believe that more is better than enough. Many of the British population of World War II who were already eating enough vitamin A were probably forced into conformity unnecessarily when they allowed themselves to be compelled to eat carrots, which they did not like, as a source of supplementary vitamin A activity. It was even reported that a few enthusiasts became yellow with a complaint, carotenaemia, due to excessive consumption of carrots, and required medical treatment.

Knowledge of vitamin D and its preventive action against rickets has been one of the single most beneficial advances in paediatrics. When Mrs Beaton wrote her famous cookery book in the reign of Queen Victoria, there was no way of feeding an infant satisfactorily other than on mother's milk. Failing this or a wet-nurse, Mrs Beaton recommended ass's milk. Today, food technology can provide very adequate formulae upon which infants grow and thrive. These contain vitamin D. Too much vitamin D may, however, lead to danger. In 1952, a new disease, idiopathic hypercalcaemia of infants, was described in

London which was strongly suspected as being due to a well-meant excess of vitamin D in the British Welfare Foods for babies.

Rich technological societies attach themselves to complex scientific products such as frozen green peas and breakfast cereals, the offshoots of intricate scientific processes. Or again, a strong addiction is developed for canned pineapples and mayonnaise. Food items such as these can only be produced by the use of elaborate machinery, an understanding of bio-chemistry, bacteriology and plant genetics. The power of this sort of addiction was forcibly shown by the British in 1940. At this time, food supplies for Great Britain were only imported at the heavy cost of ships and men's lives. Dried egg and concentrated orange juice had to run the gauntlet of bombs and torpedoes on the high seas. Yet it was shown by Professor McCance and his collaborator, Dr Elsie Widdowson, that the need for this heavy sacrifice in blood and treasure could largely be avoided by the consumption of a largely indigenous diet of black bread, cabbage and milk. To demonstrate that this diet contained all the scientific nutrients necessary for health and well-being, the intrepid investigators lived on it themselves for a prolonged period during which they undertook strenuous exertions. Except for some transient flatulence, their health remained unimpaired. Yet their compatriots' addiction to technological foods caused them to reject the economical diet proposed by McCance and Widdowson.

Perhaps, however, at some time in the not too distant future another aspect of modern technology may bring about a change. Science and technology are with ever increasing momentum making the world smaller. The units of industry become bigger and fewer. The world's fats are handled now by one predominant company and so are the tropical fruits. While this is happening, the same forces press the smaller political units together into large confederations. If this process should continue we shall see dietetic uniformity, at present restricted to individual countries, extended to cover these much larger mergers. It is quite feasible to distribute baked beans, ice-cream or cornflakes uniformly throughout a single country. When a country is extended, however, to include a couple of continents, this may not be possible—there will not be enough beans or cornflakes, and there will be too many people. Then we can expect the strong pressure of science to insist that black bread and cabbage—rendered attractive, let us hope, by technological ingenuity—or some other combination of indigenous foods shall be accepted.

8

STRETCHED BY TRAVEL

FOR MOST of human history the speed of locomotion remained much the same and depended on the pace at which a
horse could travel. Very satisfactory civilisations were able to
develop without the need or the capacity to go any faster. The
Romans organised their considerable empire using the horse
as their means of communication by providing an adequate
road system for it to travel over. Pepys in the seventeenth
century described an urbane and complex society enjoying
much of what we consider today to be valuable and cultured
but without any means of travel more rapid than that of a
thousand years before. Dr Johnson a hundred years later could
talk and write in London and travel through Scotland and the
Hebrides at a pace no faster than that of Pepys. And then,
suddenly at the beginning of the nineteenth century came
the age of technology in which we are now living. Of all
the aspects of this new age, the one that has probably had the
greatest impact on individual men and women has been the
enormously accelerated possibilities of human locomotion.

Consider what the inhabitants of a large modern city have
trained themselves to endure. Between half past eight and half
past nine in the morning the commuters' trains pour in, each
crowded with people. These several thousands of men and
women, tense, not speaking to each other, intellectually hold-
ing their breath until the operation is over and they come to
rest in their offices and factories, are passed into the town by
the transport authorities in exactly the same way that mass-
produced commodities are handled in a well-run plant. The
procedure in technical terms is called 'materials handling'.

In the days before serious thought was given to the problem,
sacks of wheat were carried into the mill one by one on men's

shoulders. Then, a few years ago, it was found to be more efficient to use a movable mechanical conveyor by means of which the sacks could be shifted by a travelling belt from the vehicle in which they had arrived on to the permanent conveyor system in the mill. This identical process is also applied to human material. The similarity between the components in a factory being moved from place to place on travelling belts and the movement of commuters jostling along a platform, pressing pell-mell through the gap in a barrier, and then moved smoothly and efficiently along the conveyor-belt of an escalator is almost too striking to need comment.

The human animal is a remarkably hardy and adaptable creature, which, of course, is one of the reasons why he has come to dominate biological creation and been able to inhabit so wide an area of the earth comprising so various a range of climatic conditions. Although it must be considered a hardship to be compelled twice a day to submit to the disagreeable physical ordeal of congested travel from a house to a factory or office situated anything up to fifty miles away, it would, perhaps, be hard to demonstrate that this process produces any positive physical harm. Again, the grinding cold of the long Moscow winter necessitates inhabiting a stuffy unventilated room by night and hurrying through the bitter streets by day wrapped up so as to be barely able to move; all this must impose considerable stress, yet many Moscovites are healthy and vigorous. To take a third example, proponents of brown bread have suggested that those who eat white bread are subjecting themselves to physiological attack from the three-fold stress of lack of vitamins, harm from toxic substances in the white flour, and inadequate bulk for the health of the intestines; these three assertions are hard to substantiate, yet, even assuming they do exist, recent detailed reviews of the scientific facts fail to show that any permanent physical harm results from a lifetime's consumption of white bread.

The crowded, rushing travel of the urban citizen of our modern technological society, while it may not harm the

'. . . the human animal has come to dominate biological creation . . .'

traveller's body, must inevitably weary and depress his mind. The loss of two or three hours each day under disagreeable and frustrating conditions must surely be attributed as a hardship imposed by the modern way of life.

It is interesting to consider whether the submissive, indrawn and silent commuters, jostling and bumping each other as they pass along the channels designed by the technological experts of the urban transport department—just like cans of beans in a modern cannery or beer bottles in a mechanised brewery—will be happier or less happy in the future. The first stage in applying the scientific principles of materials handling to moving sacks of grain was to devise mechanical means of moving the sacks. That is to say, instead of there being a man carrying a sack on his shoulders, there was a belt, or the pocket in a moving sling, that carried out the same operation. In other words, the man had been automated. In principle, the escalator in a railway station does for the passengers what they previously did for themselves, namely it carries them upstairs. But when the engineers had had an opportunity to consider the problem of shifting a load of grain, they very soon developed the present more advanced system used today in which the grain is never put in sacks at all but is moved in bulk and transferred pneumatically through pipes by being blown or sucked by compressed air. Let the travellers beware.

The well-being of an individual man or woman depends on two groups of factors. The first, to which a predominant proportion of scientific attention has been given, is the maintenance of health. This is achieved by the possession of a satisfactory genetical background, which in ordinary language implies having healthy parents. In addition, there must be an absence of harmful infections, the provision of reasonably satisfactory surroundings, adequate housing, freedom from such undesirable factors as excessive noise, or damp, or radio-activity, and the availability of sufficient calories, protein, minerals and vitamins—that is to say, enough of the right combination of foods to eat. But besides all this, there must be an adequately organised human community. In scientific terms, this implies that due deference is paid to the principles of animal ecology.

A sponge may have given our grandparents, who used it as an adjunct to a satisfactory hot bath on a Saturday night, the impression that it was a single entity. In its natural form, anchored to a rock at the bottom of the sea, however, it can better be considered as a closely knit community rather than a single creature. The numerous cells making up the whole, though intimately dependent one on the other, can also each be viewed as separate entities. It is possible to press a living sponge through a sieve and thus divide the colony into the separate individuals of which it is composed. If when this is done the separated units are all allowed to congregate close together in warm sea water, a sponge as we know it will re-form and continue living. Only if a fairly large number of individual sponge cells are permitted to come together will this occur. If the individual living cells are scattered about so that groups may only be formed from a few members, all will gradually die away.

This behaviour may be reproduced by human communities. When an adequate number of individuals gather to form a social unit, there will be sufficient diverse personalities present to produce a vigorous society with theatres and concerts, an active football club, schools, a university perhaps, a shopping centre, churches of various denominations and all the different enthusiasms that make it a lively going concern. The community in very truth is alive and draws people to it—like a sponge. There is, however, a minimum size to such a group. When the members become too few, the human colony disintegrates like a sparse assembly of sponge cells. The main object of one man alone—Robinson Crusoe, let us say—is to escape from his solitude. And in our present age of technological civilisation, even a family of man, wife and children is too small a contingent to be prepared to exist willingly on their own. Improbable as is the story of the ingenious and conscientious Swiss Family Robinson, their logical Victorian author did not seriously expect us to believe that they would have stayed on their island on their own once the opportunity to return to Europe had presented itself.

The laws of the biological science of human ecology can to-day be seen working themselves out in the Hebridean Islands of Scotland. The small communities on these islands are too few to provide the minimum needs that members of a techno-logical society demand for a good life. Besides the lack of tele-vision, there are often inadequate schools and insufficient diversity of interests. And gradually, like the too small sponges, these communities die away, the islands become depopulated and the villages derelict.

Before technology was applied to transport, people lived in towns and villages of which they were an organic part. Many people are still able to do this today. There are the small towns, which it is sometimes thought fashionable to decry, in which there are, living and working, a diverse group of men and women who together comprise a vigorous viable ecological entity. These societies have sometimes learned to cope with the potentially disruptive modern forces of technology applied to transport. A motorcar, a railway train or an aeroplane is a use-ful human servant when it is used to enrich the possibilities of life by being employed only occasionally and for consciously selected purposes.

It is convenient for a student to be able to jump into an auto-mobile—the last word in engineering expertise—and drive himself to a university, but the acquisition of learning for which he goes there would be as well served if the motorcar had never been invented. A craftsman seeking work away from home is not baulked of his purpose if he travels to the new town slowly—even on foot. The rapid transport, made possible by the highest complexities of engineering science, that has gripped the huge numbers who sleep in one place, travel to work in another, and then travel back to sleep, is a Procrustean artifice that is breaking down the harmony of normal human ecology. Many of the towns in our technological communities appear to be big enough to compromise a viable community—many of them seem to be far too big. But these towns are often mirages, denuded of social reality by the technology of modern travel.

The social destruction of modern communities is, of course, due to the fact that many of the people whose houses are situated in them do not in fact 'live' there. The most striking example of this ghostly reality is seen in the new towns and suburbs. The husbands travel off—efficiently, swiftly, sometimes in tolerable comfort—and the wives left in the clean modern houses may find themselves bereft of the ecological support they need. In an old community that has grown over a period of years there are grandmothers and aunts and familiar places to which people are attached by genuine living social ties. These old towns may have been lacking in technological amenities but the families in them *lived* there. This was where the work was and work was then a part of 'real' life. And the technological marvels of modern transport had not been invented.

There are here and there wise and active men and women to be found who are working to find a way to rehouse people from old unsatisfactory dwellings and allow them to enjoy the gifts of modern technology—warm dry spaciousness, machines of all sorts: for washing, cleaning, providing amusement, music or refrigeration—without at the same time breaking up the close-knit 'sponge' of interlocking human relationships. But it is so much easier to design and erect a block of old people's dwellings, each with the desired provision of 'amenities', than it is to dismantle an existing, technologically unsatisfactory slum, and reassemble it so that there shall be, simultaneously, adequate space and a sufficient number of warm hearts in a hundred families so that 'granny' may serve her family while she can and be cared for lovingly when she is no longer able. What is most difficult of all is to resist the centripetal force of a large town drawing factories and offices into it and thus filling a larger and larger area in the centre with industrial non-life to which great numbers must travel and from which they must each day travel back.

In the Procrustean legend, the robber cut off pieces of his victim if he was too large to fit inside the Bedstead. When dealing with a modern urban community he does the very same. The boulevards and highways to carry the streams of motorcars, six abreast, into and out of the cities cut these very cities into pieces. Railway lines divide the community into quarters and create iron barriers almost as impervious as international frontiers. To be born on the wrong side of the tracks is equivalent to carrying the wrong kind of passport. The previously living community has its members separated in two ways. In the first place, the working members are only half there because the complex transport system efficiently performs its functions and shuttles them away. And, on the other hand, the transport mechanism itself dismembers the town. Hence, like the dismembered sponge, the life of the community is stricken by these cuts.

It would be ungrateful to paint the picture all black. The modern societies have very much to be grateful for. An automobile allows its owner to enrich his life by enjoying every variety of experience to be had within hundreds of miles around. The trade of the world enables nations to enjoy the fruits of every land—provided that problems of payment can be overcome, and these are usually not considered to be the business of science. This trade is carried in almost unsinkable ships driven by engines comprising prodigies of engineering skill and invention and using as motive power coal, oil and now the newly-won forces of the heart and core of matter: nuclear energy. Nevertheless, the problem is how, while enjoying the benefits of mechanised motion, to avoid the painful stress it brings with it.

Joachim Leithauser has pointed out that there was a time— and that time could be now if we were adroit—when the advancing technology of travel demonstrably contributed to the good life. In 1850, a man visiting, say, his father and mother a hundred and twenty miles away was called upon to endure suffocating congestion and intense discomfort in a jolting stage-coach, whose wheels were for ever getting broken and whose windows let in the draught—presuming that he was travelling inside and not out in the rain on the roof.

Leithauser paints a vivid picture of the worried traveller hurrying far more than his modern counterpart who 'has a wide choice of comfortable means of travel at all hours of the day and night'. This being in contrast to the nineteenth-century traveller who had to catch the daily stage-coach or not go at all. And even when he had caught the coach, the danger of accident was higher than that of travelling by train a hundred years or so later. Painting in the German scene, Leithauser calculates that out of every ten million stage-coach passengers in the year 1800, three hundred and thirty-three were injured and ten were killed. In 1944, on the other hand, only four railway passengers were injured and one was killed. Dickens did not go into statistics as thoroughly as this nor did he take the situation quite so seriously, yet talking of England in 1837, Mr Pickwick in his speech to the Pickwick Club described the situation as follows:

> He could not but feel that they had selected him for a service of great honour, and of some danger. Travelling was in a troubled state, and the minds of coachmen were unsettled. Let them look abroad and contemplate the scenes which were enacting around them. Stage coaches were upsetting in all directions, horses were bolting, boats were overturning, and boilers were bursting. (Cheers—a voice, 'No'.)

And then railways were invented and the perhaps slightly idealised state of affairs described by Leithauser supervened.

I have already referred to the way in which even the so-safe railway lines may become part of the strains of life whose discomfort must be borne twice a day by city dwellers travelling to and from their work. More lethal than steam and diesel traction, however, is the internal combustion engine that has now followed in the march of technological advance.

Dr L. G. Norman, Chief Medical Officer of the London Transport Executive, has pointed out that the first two deaths registered in Great Britain as due to motorcars were in 1896, while the first men to be killed by motorcycles died in 1902. But from these small beginnings, Procrustes has now increased his toll to a significant percentage of the population. By 1960, or so Dr Norman has calculated, 125,000 members of the British population had been killed because of the internal combustion engine.

In 1958, 5970 people were killed, of whom 2277 were under 30, and 69,166 were seriously injured. These numbers would represent a major epidemic were they due to disease—and such a disease! killing more of the young than the old. But this was no ordinary public-health problem. It is a chop of Procrustes' knife to make the British community fit the Technological Bedstead in which they have chosen to lie. The total number of casualties of all sorts—dead, seriously injured and just injured—gives an interesting view of the extent of the mutilation that the British community of about fifty million people is prepared to suffer from this special aspect of technology, namely, motor transport. In 1935, 220,000 people were involved; in 1955, 268,000; and in 1958, the number was 299,797!

This painful effect of the modern scene affects the community in a particularly sensitive part. Of all the young men in the years of promise between 20 and 24 who die in Great Britain, a third falls victim to the motorcar. Technological deaths of men on British roads are more numerous than those due to tuberculosis, diabetes, chronic rheumatic heart disease and peptic ulcers. The total situation is summed up in the calculation that during the safest years of their lives, between 35 and 65, out of every 100,000 men, 3000 will suffer in a severe traffic accident.

The attractions of speed and comfort derived from the scientific and technological advances of our modern age are very great. Yet the price is high. Road accidents are now the commonest cause of death for adolescent boys and young men and women. The most direct way to avoid this harm would be to arrange modern life so that there was less travelling to do. When his car has travelled 200,000 miles, the average British driver has an accident. Two hundred thousand miles seems a long way, but the journey comes to an end at last. Five seconds or less are needed for the development of an accident.

Is it not possible to avoid the blow by improving the reaction-times of people who use automobiles? A great deal of attention has been paid to this possibility. Drinking makes the reaction-time slower; it is, therefore, rational to require that it must not be indulged in by those who drive mechanical vehicles. It seems obvious, as Dr Norman has pointed out, that drivers with the shortest reaction-time should be able to act most promptly in the accident situation and thus have fewer accidents than more slowly-reacting drivers. Unfortunately life is more complicated than scientific and technological logic sometimes assumes (as, indeed, it is the thesis of this book to show). Although drivers between 18 and 25 have the shortest reaction-times, they are involved in many more accidents than middle-aged drivers. In all sorts of tests of psycho-kinetic performance, the young drivers do better than the older ones. It seems, however, that as a man ages, his reactions become slower, his hearing gets dim and the co-ordination of his eye and hand deteriorates—yet he becomes a safer driver.

This is discouraging to those scientific investigators who are trying to find means of avoiding the painful consequences of the successes of the other scientists who have made it possible to speed through the country without changing gear. The 'tapping test', the 'simulated driving test' in a 'motor trainer', laboratory and field studies of diverse kinds, all these can give results of great precision, yet the middle-aged drivers who keep alive on the road do so not because of any superior acuity or quickness but because thay have a knack of avoiding the accident situation. Somehow, care, experience and a quality of being able to anticipate keep them out of trouble.

The psychologists too have had a disappointing time. Like other scientists who have investigated the matter, they also have applied a variety of tests to see how best to stop people being killed while enjoying mechanical transport. Tests of eye-hand co-ordination, of 'choice-reaction', of psycho-social and temperamental factors, have all been applied. At last it seemed that some progress was being made. It was discovered that people who tended to come to harm possessed the person-ality characteristics of 'egocentricity, aggressiveness, anti-social trends, and social irresponsibility'. But just at this point when, we may assume, the psychologists were about to recom-mend that drivers with these qualities should be kept away from motorcars, the curious anomaly was discovered 'that some people who are quite reasonable in ordinary life become unreasonable when driving a motor vehicle'. And so, after all their efforts the psychologists can do no better than summarise the results of their scientific studies in the following aphorism: 'a man drives as he lives'. In the light of our observations on how men live in the modern technological world, this is not particularly helpful.

These stresses of life may fall unexpectedly and cause dis-aster to a man seemingly armed at every point. Professor Bartlett, for example, described a state of 'skill fatigue'. It seems that during the first hours when a man is required to do work that calls for concentration and precision he may suffer from 'skill fatigue'. Bartlett gives as a typical example the man driving at night who 'halts at an intersection where there is no traffic light and waits patiently for the green; then, pulling himself together, he dashes on, intent on the clear roadway ahead, and deriving no meaning from the headlights he sees approaching from the side'.

While the psychologists are considering whether it is within their power to shield people from the lethal effects of techno-logical travel, the pharmacologists have also been turning their minds to the problem. Today, there are available a variety of new and powerful drugs that can achieve all sorts of effects, from lowering the blood pressure to changing the whole personality. Dr S. E. Millar, writing from Michigan, has suggested that long-distance lorry drivers who, it appears, are particularly exposed to fatigue and depression, might consider taking doses of the drug, amphetamine, which can be expected to increase their alertness and efficiency, at least for a couple of hours or so. Unfortunately, too much amphetamine causes 'headache, agitation, irritability and impaired concentration'— just what one does not want in a lorry driver—and there are, therefore, other scientific experts who think it better that he should take his chances without any drugs at all. Hypnotics, sedatives, tranquillisers—all have been considered but again the pharmacological experts, like the psychologists before them, are driven to the conclusion that a man drives as he lives. Nowadays, men live in pursuit of scientific progress and this pursuit leads them to positions of stress and danger.

Yet even so, the scientists struggle to mitigate the heavy blows that are inflicted on the social body through the re-markable advances of mechanised travel. The figures from the United States, the country furthest advanced in technical cul-ture, show how heavy these blows may become. In the U.S.A., about 4,700,000 injuries a year are caused by automobiles, and one person in ten of the American population is sacrificed every four years. And so it happens that physiologists, as well as the psychologists and pharmacologists about whom I have already written, are also making their studies of the matter.

One of the ways in which industrial busyness claims its victims is by causing the users of all sorts of mechanical vehicles, trucks, automobiles, and sometimes aeroplanes as well, to fall asleep. The physiologists who want to stop this happen-ing have carried out some remarkably thorough investigations. It seems that it is not a simple matter of fatigue that makes the drivers go to sleep and while sleeping kill themselves. Partly it is the movement of the machine—the direct result of the technical operation by which it is made to go at all—that makes the men fall into their slumber. The scientists have examined the matter in detail. The cab of a motor lorry is constructed in the laboratory and the sample driver put into it. The cab is then caused to vibrate at varying speeds, with different degrees of amplitude, evenly, unevenly, up and down or, perhaps, with some measure of transverse motion. The results of this work show that when subjected to certain types of vibration of low amplitude the drivers fall asleep. The effect is, in fact, in the technological context of a road vehicle throbbing ceaselessly along the endless highways of today, a version of the effect sought by a mother rocking a cradle. She too is applying a certain kind of vibration of low amplitude.

But road vehicles are not the whole problem. Whereas the toll runs into thousands from this form of transport now, tomorrow it may strike the travellers in jets and super-jets and rockets. These new and potentially possible means of locomotion subject those who propose to use them to different kinds of vibrations. There are, in consequence, a number of scientific centres where there are investigators who are making it their business to find out what the effect of these new stresses will be and how best they may be resisted. For example, dogs or other small animals can be vibrated in measured amount and a study made to see whether by feeding them more or less, or more protein and less fat, or increased vitamins or reduced calcium—whether one or other of these changes can assist them to resist the effects of being ceaselessly shaken, shaken, shaken, like a lorry driver, or the pilot of an aircraft with propellers, or an aircraft with jets, or like a man all wrapped up and lying crouched in a projectile trembling in some entirely novel way.

The investigators are making progress, but whether it is directly applicable to current problems is more difficult to see. For example, if the dogs are starved of protein they resist the effects of being vibrated better than normally fed dogs. But the researchers go steadily on. They shake the dogs more and more and find that they take up more oxygen into their tissues; other workers examine the dogs' blood sugar (it does not change), and so on.

But the studies of vibration, to which we must all submit in the enjoyment of modern travel, are not restricted to dogs and truck drivers. For example, there is on record a study of what happens when expectant mothers are vibrated. And why not? All of us are in this together; it is the community that has submitted itself to the Technological Life, and every member must, therefore, learn how to protect himself—or herself.

Perhaps the next step in our progress will provide a solution to the whole problem. This, of course, will be space travel. It would be foolish to ignore what is involved just because this particular 'Atlantic' is only now being flown for the first time. When Alcock and Brown flapped their way from Newfoundland to Ireland in 1919, and even when eight years later Lindbergh flew from New York to Paris, normal people did not really believe that this kind of thing would become a matter-of-fact means of travel. But just as transatlantic flying became commonplace within a few years, we must now suppose that the dramatic development of space travel of 1961 will soon be just one more step in the modern technological advance for every man.

We can already glimpse something of the adjustments that will be demanded of the people who submit themselves to this means of transport. The Martin Company of Denver, Colorado, which builds the Titan inter-continental missile, has already advanced far in the development of a space vehicle seriously intended for travel to the moon and the planets. While the engineers and ballistic experts are busy with the mechanics of launching and navigation, a group of other specialists has been studying 'space ecology', that is the science of living while travelling in space. In order to do this they are constructing a full-sized space unit in which a crew of men can live for months completely self-contained, under conditions resembling as closely as possible those likely to be encountered in space or on the Moon. If anyone else wants to join in these studies, the Martin Company is prepared to sell them a 'lunar housing simulator' so that they can practise too.

This non-flying model is a sphere thirty-two feet in diameter enclosed in a shell fifty-seven feet across, with the space between completely emptied of air. The crew can practise climbing out of the air-lock in the inner ball into this vacuum area in order to get used to doing repairs while dressed in space-suits. It is planned that a crew of five will live and sleep and eat in this little isolated world for months on end.

It is unnecessary for me to discuss in detail the various adaptations that people need to make if they desire to travel by space-ship. Perhaps, however, it is worth while at least to enumerate them because, taken as a whole, these various stresses when put together make up something worth thinking about. Just as town dwellers in up-to-date technological communities have to bear the mental stresses of shutting off their minds from the 'oxygen' of normal human intercourse during the period of each day when, packed like sardines, they shuttle backwards and forwards between their work and their home, so does the space traveller suffer in the same way but to a greatly intensified degree. When gravity ceases to operate upon him and he floats like a bubble in his capsule—or would do if he were not strapped in—things begin to happen to his mind. The conditions in which he is existing are those of 'sensory deprivation'.

People who are members of a lively community enjoy the play and interplay of each other's ideas, of assessing each other's behaviour. From the middle-aged spinsters of the village who gain their main enjoyment of life from watching the world go by through the lace curtains of their parlour window, all the way to the brilliant Ph.D. who struggles to gain a place in the small select community of a chosen department of a special university—just because Professor X or Doctor Y has a group of distinguished people round him there—human individuals acquire a major part of their life force from the community of which they are a part. But it now appears that not only do they feed their minds with ideas—of what is going on in the village, or what new ideas are developing in science—and so keep mentally alive so far as higher intellectual matters are concerned, but that all the minor trivial impacts of environment, the tickling of one's clothing, the feel of the ground underfoot, the tightness of one's collar, the sound of birds or traffic, the smell of the town and changing movement of what we see around us, this ceaseless flickering of our senses keeps us sane, normal and at one with our environment. There is good evidence that too long a deprivation of all this in the weightless uniformity of a space-ship's cabin may have a permanent effect on the traveller's sanity. The now demoted term 'lunatic' may need to be reintroduced to describe a successful traveller to the moon.

But the space traveller will find two other simple needs which will bring him more directly to reconsider his attitude to the Technological Society as a whole. These are the needs for oxygen and for food.

During the evolution of the earth the early atmosphere was devoid of oxygen. The living creatures on the planet at that time maintained life by dealing with the nutrients they used for food by a process of fermentation, which does not require oxygen, just as yeast and other microbes still do, rather than by respiration as is our habit today. It is generally accepted by most scientists that the entire oxygen of the present atmosphere owes its origin to photosynthesis by green plants which evolved at a later stage in the earth's history. And so it comes about that the technological experts of the Martin Company of Colorado, and the other places where men are busy creating new 'planets', have decided that if the vehicles are to be self-supporting for oxygen, the best way to go about it is to install some sort of green plants in them. In their experiments they have already been able to keep a mouse in a sealed chamber in which all its oxygen is supplied by a brew of a specially selected strain of algae. The activity of the algae is such that two and a half quarts of the algal solution represent 'four mouse-power'. The quantity sufficient for 'one man-power' is merely a matter of arithmetic.

Besides oxygen, the space travellers will need food. And now that it is being seriously considered that they can obtain the oxygen they want from algae, it is a short step to the conclusion that this, a primitive but economical vegetable, might serve them for food as well. The total operation involves the following steps: the space traveller breathes in oxygen and breathes out carbon dioxide. The broth of green algae absorbs the carbon dioxide and, using the energy of the sunlight shining in through the windows of the space-ship, splits it up, releases the oxygen again and, by consuming the carbon part of the carbon dioxide, grows. The man in the space-ship then eats the surplus algae and uses the remainder in the tank as a means of disposing of sewage, by which means the algae is stimulated to grow the more, re-process oxygen more vigorously and keep the whole operation in motion.

This is the theory of space travel. As yet, however, it has not been achieved fully in practice. To start with, the algal paste is not particularly inviting to eat and, besides, it is not certain that it contains all the nutrients a man needs for, say, a six-month voyage. So the Martin Company people are experimenting with ordinary garden vegetables, grown on ash to be sure, but fertilised as before.

In modern life we suffer strains and tensions from the numbers of people who crowd into the cities to enjoy the pleasures of Technology. Adequate up-to-date sewage disposal is one of these pleasures. But when something goes wrong—the kitchen sink gets plugged up, or the city of New York begins to notice that the colour of the ocean six miles off the coast is changing due to the masses of city refuse dumped into it—then we feel a twinge. To take advantage of the most advanced form of transport that science can offer—space travel—we have to allow ourselves to be refitted into a quite remarkable shape. Space travellers, the most technologically sophisticated of all mankind, may find it necessary, in order to manage the new planets in which they will be flying, to return to the most primitive form of living of the remotest past.

For short journeys—say to the Moon and back and no more —they might be able to take their more sophisticated comforts with them: oxygen in cylinders and food in cans. Scientific studies of space travel talk about the 'cross-over point' when the length of the proposed journey makes it just worth while to make the crew self-supporting of atmosphere and food rather than having to take supplies with them. At one time the 'cross-over point' used to be thought to occur at six months, but experts now believe that it may be as short as twenty days. This dwindling estimate of the 'cross-over' time comes about because, although the use of carried rations—corned beef, jam, biscuits, and the like—may seem more attractive than the algal diet, its consumption presents certain problems. For example, how will the travellers dispose of sewage? Small objects thrown out of a space ship may revolve round it like moons, held by the force of gravity, until the journey is over. This would clearly be undesirable.

Thus the transport rocket, with its community of travellers, must grow its own food, whether as algae or something else, and must depend on the green things it grows for the oxygen the voyagers in space require for their breathing. The inexorable pressure of technological necessity is forcing the rocket engineers to model the vehicles they are building on the state of affairs existing on Earth. Our oxygen and our food are produced on this space-ship, the Earth, in just the way that the Martin Company is proposing to arrange them. Perhaps, as the engineers think more and more deeply about how to insure the physical comfort and well-being of the rocket travellers, and how to protect them from 'sensory deprivation', and how to prevent their quarrelling—clearly, something that must be avoided at all costs—their conclusions may one day be applicable to affairs down here on this terrestrial space-ship where conditions are almost as crowded, where technical devices are becoming almost as numerous, and where the need to live comfortably and harmoniously together with the other travellers is every bit as great.

9

THE CAMEL, THE FERRET
AND THE TIT

WHEN LIFE seems to be becoming almost intolerable and we
feel that we can no longer bear to curb our natural behaviour to
avoid being mutilated in the factory machines; when the incessant din of patriotic exhortation, of appeals to buy motorcars, television sets and food, become almost overwhelming;
and when it seems an insult to our personalities to allow ourselves to be conveyed on escalators, trans-shipped in subways
and directed in droves by efficient, elegant but unfeeling young
women into and out of aeroplanes—when we feel that this is
beginning to happen, let us turn to the animal creation and see
whether we can learn from the beasts.

Of all creatures on earth, the camel has contorted itself and
its internal metabolism most effectively, one might think, in
order to cope with an environment that is of all others particularly difficult to endure. It lives under a blinding sun without shade. Yet it copes with the roasting temperature without
complaint or harm. It has accustomed itself to eat dry and
prickly food. Its most valuable adaptation has been to develop
a way, through the generations, of husbanding its supplies of
water so as to be able to function under conditions of desicca-
tion sufficient to make a man fall prostrate and die. Our
environment has its own hardships: if a man allows his mind to
wander only for a moment and forget the lifelong training by
which he has learned to live, let him step into the city roadway without thinking and he will be dead. How does the camel
live with the exigencies of *its* environment?

To start with—and this is a lesson for us—it does not take
the easy way out. Something much more subtle is required.
Pliny the Elder assumed that the camel could go for long

periods without water because it had a reservoir somewhere inside it. Modern textbooks have also propagated this notion—which is quite wrong—by the normal process of textbook writing, which is to copy from several earlier textbooks. The only innovation has been to change the position of the imaginary reservoir from the camel's stomach to its hump.

When Professor Schmidt-Nielsen went out to the Sahara in 1953 and slaughtered a camel, he found when he had dissected it that it did not in fact possess any special internal container for storing water. True, a camel is capable of drinking very quickly and can consume twenty-seven gallons in ten minutes, but this is explicable on the basis that it is thirsty. When such a camel is killed, all its tissues and organs contain the normal amount of water.

How, then, does the camel do it? How does it survive for months without water during the Saharan winter? How did Professor Schmidt-Nielsen's camel survive eight days without drinking in the heat of the desert summer with the day temperature at 120°F or more? There are several answers to these questions. The first—and this is applicable to man's situation in a technological environment—is that the camel is calm and goes about its business no matter how torrid the weather. Without water a camel loses weight, it sweats, it loses water in its breath and in its urine, but if there is food for it to eat—even dry food—it eats it.

The camel has acquired from its heredity two special qualities that enable it to go on under the adverse conditions under which it lives. The first quality is the ability to select from two alternatives the one of crucial importance. If a man is lost in the desert without water until at last twenty-five per cent of the moisture in his body has been lost and dried up, his blood will lose a third of its volume and will become too thick and viscous to circulate through his veins—and he will die. A camel, on the other hand, can afford to lose twenty-five per cent of its body moisture. It does this by so organising things that the larger loss is of the fluid in its tissues and the volume of its blood therefore only diminishes by a tenth. Under these circumstances, its blood continues freely circulating and the camel goes on living.

Besides using its biological wisdom to choose right, that is to sacrifice water from its tissues rather than from its blood under the desiccating influence of the desert sun, the camel exhibits another useful characteristic for dealing with its rigorous environment. It has brought itself to be flexible. It 'swings with the punch'. The laws of biology apply to all: to camels equally as to men. To protect its vital organs from becoming too hot it has to sweat. But sweating involves a loss of the water that it cannot afford to lose. To save this loss the camel postpones sweating to the last possible moment. It plods along as the heat increases until its temperature has risen too—in fact, the camel allows its temperature to get to fever heat at 105°F, before it checks the rise by sweating. This delay, uncomfortable though it may be, saves water. Furthermore, its hereditary abilities allow it to show even greater ingenuity. At night, when the sands of the desert grow cold, the camel allows itself to cool off as well, until its temperature is down as low as 93°F. By this means most of the day will have passed before its body heats up to 105°F and so it need waste almost no water in sweating.

Apart from the moral lesson set us by the camel's example —to choose wisely in our own desert which losses of human personality we may consider expendable and can allow the rigours of technology to take from us and which are vital to life, and to bend flexibly to the diurnal pressures of modern life that cannot be avoided and cool off in the evenings—apart from this, there are some direct biological lessons to be learned.

Donkeys in the Sahara manage to make do in the heat fairly well, but they cannot emulate the camel. That is, they cannot run a high temperature by day and a low temperature by night and, for this reason, they have to drink more frequently than the camel does. Similarly, a man cannot achieve this useful biological trick either. But it would be worth while to find out whether some people can allow their temperatures to move up and down in a wider margin than others, because these would be the people best suited to dig for oil in French Equatorial Africa or wherever else of a similar climate to which technology might lead.

There is another respect in which the biological lesson of the camel might help a man to cope with the pressures of technological life. A principal duty of the modern citizen is to tend to the needs of machines. The cost of the complex mechanisms by which goods are automatically produced is so great that, not requiring sleep, they must never be allowed to stay idle so that the expense of their installation may be the sooner repaid. And since the machines must work at night, so must the men who look after them. Unfortunately, there are certain people who suffer if they are compelled to work, week about, at night. For them, the night shift represents another racking of the Procrustean screw.

Take the temperature of a camel on a cold night and it is down to 93°F; at the height of the day it is 105°F. Do the same for a man and you will find in the dead of night his temperature is 97°F and at mid-day it is 99°F. There is, in fact, a rhythm. But when a man is made to change from working by day and sleeping by night to a night shift when he must work at night and sleep during the day, he will be unhappy and unwell until he succeeds in reversing his rhythm.

Man is not alone in the possession of a physiological rhythm. The sensitive mimosa unfolds its leaves in the daylight and folds them again at night. And it goes on doing this even if it is placed in a windowless room with the electric light left on all the time. The marine invertebrate, *Actinia equina*, retracts its tentacles and closes its sphincter each twelve hours when the tide goes out. It, too, goes on extending and retracting its tentacles and opening and closing its sphincter for some considerable time after it has been put into an aquarium. The temperature rhythm of human beings goes on too for a time that may be quite prolonged even if their daily routine becomes disrupted by the needs of work or travel.

Professor Kleitman showed some years ago when he carried out his classical experiments in Mammoth Caves, Kentucky, that certain individuals are able to break their physiological rhythm if circumstances demand and fit it to the new time-table which industrial work or the calls of other duties may be imposing. Other people may possess awkward and individualistic physiological mechanisms which are not prepared to adapt to the imposed demands of industrial life so readily. These people may find themselves resisting their communities' demands for uniformity with their bodies as well as their minds.

The direct lesson of Professor Kleitman's experiment seems to be that certain types of people are better suited to fit themselves to certain particular restrictions. If the technological situation demands that men and women should work to a rotation of night shifts, or should serve in ships and aeroplanes oscillating between London and Melbourne, or New York and Hong Kong, it is prudent to enquire whether the particular people chosen for these jobs are temperamentally suited to them. It is surely a matter of technical inefficiency to engage people for a task at which they are likely to break down— quite apart from the suffering inflicted by trying to use such unsuitable living tools.

It is fascinating to speculate how far the behaviour of the beasts can help the members of the technological communities in which we live today to adapt themselves to the more abrupt strains of their environment.

Can ferrets, I wonder, teach us anything? A female ferret has a six-weeks' pregnancy and, for the good of its young, it is important that its families should be born in the spring and summer. It is, therefore, equipped with a built-in physiological mechanism whereby when the length of the light of daytime is longer than the dark time of night, the ferret's eyes, recording this fact, pass on the information to the hypothalamous and thence to the pituitary. The pituitary thus stimulated releases a hormone into the blood stream which acts on the ovaries and so brings the animal into the breeding state. The spring and summer pass and the ferret brings up two litters of its young. But now the nights are longer than the days. The signal that is picked up by the ferret's eyes—shorter light flashes (if a 'flash' can be eight hours long) and longer dark intervals—causes a decline in the activity of the pituitary and brings the breeding season to an end.

The horse behaves like the ferret. It also has found that it can best meet the exigencies of the climate in which it lives if it produces its young in the early summer rather than in the cold of the winter. Consequently, it is organised to respond to longer light periods alternating with shorter dark periods. The mare therefore becomes pregnant in the summer when this interchange of light and dark exists. But whereas the ferret with a six-weeks' period of gestation produces young the same summer, the mare that has an eleven-months' pregnancy brings out her foal the next spring. But besides the ferret and the horse, there are creatures that have come to be adjusted the other way round. Sheep, for example—and, for that matter, goats as well—have a five-months' pregnancy. Consequently, if their eyes told their hypothalamous to tell their pituitary to release follicle-stimulating hormones and stimulate the development of eggs in their ovaries when the days were longer than the nights, the lambs and kids would be born just as winter was setting in. These species, therefore, have equipped themselves with a physiological control mechanism which is triggered off when the length of the light period of day is shorter than that of the dark period of night: that is to say, in the second half of the summer. It is then that they mate, so that it follows that their young are born only when the winter is over and spring on the way.

It is tempting to think that we can learn to fit ourselves too to the technological surroundings in which we live. Surely this would need only a little study and consideration. The sheep, like ourselves, has to cope with technological problems as well as the more basic matters of winter and summer climate of the place where it is born. Within the single species, sheep, the breeds which have been moved to higher latitudes either in the northern or the southern hemisphere to meet the technical requirements of the meat industry have developed a greater sensitivity to the unbalance between the light and dark periods of day and night and have consequently a longer latent period and a shorter breeding season than those that live in more temperate parts of the world at lower latitudes. True, this has been achieved over a period of generations but it is never-theless an example of creatures fitting themselves to meet a technological demand—for example, the production of mutton by British meat producers in the Falkland Island De-pendencies south of Cape Horn—and to do this in compara-tive comfort.

But perhaps neither the ferret nor the horse, the sheep nor even the camel provides us with as provocative a moral as does the hen. The modern, high-producing hen that lays its three hundred eggs a year has of all creatures most dramatically fitted its biological functions to suit the demands of a highly-scientific industry. When the hen started its career as a wild Indian jungle fowl, it laid only a few eggs a year. And it, too, like the ferret and the horse, was stimulated to conceive by the increasing light-dark ratio of the spring. Hens can be made to lay more eggs by providing them with ample supplies of the right food. And the sexual athletes, birds that win egg-laying competitions by virtue of their natural aptitude for fecundity, have been selected by poultrymen as breeding stock. By this means, communities of prolific layers have been developed. But with these improved breeds as with the original wild fowl, there is a seasonal variation in the rate of egg-laying, and this variation is closely associated with the seasonal changes in the light-dark ratio.

As is well known, the life of the hen has been affected by science and technology to a remarkable degree. A battery hen, sitting in its carefully designed cubicle, eating its nutritionally balanced meals at set hours as the cafeteria container in which the food is carried moves round automatically on its circular track, breathing the air-conditioned atmosphere kept sweet by the mechanical removal of droppings on an endless belt, is subjected to Procrustean strains besides which those that we ourselves suffer must surely appear trifling. One of the more striking of the technological artifices imposed on the hen is to expose it to an artificially arranged light-dark ratio. This is achieved by arranging for electric lights to be automatically turned on in the hen-house by a clockwork time-switch so that the short winter days may appear to the hen to have the proportion of light and dark of the early summer that is its natural time of year for breeding.

We human beings may not be influenced by artificial lighting in the same way as hens but we are nevertheless very much affected. Indeed, the invention of first gas and then later, but more important, electric light has been one of the major factors of the technological environment in which we live.

Man is not well suited to darkness. Many of the activities which his biologically predominant mind has enabled him to develop and in which he finds peculiar enjoyment and fulfilment can only be done when there is enough light to see by. The first technological success over darkness was won in prehistoric times with the discovery of fire. It is, however, worth remembering that from the Stone Age right through human history until the nineteenth century, there was little radical change in the means of producing light. It is true that elementary firelight was improved by the development of torches soaked in pitch or resin, and that lamps with earthenware containers for fat or oil and provided with a wick were devised to give a more prolonged light. But these gave a poor flickering illumination and remained basically unchanged from the times of ancient Egypt until the French Revolution. And even then, the discovery that a lamp-glass produced a better flame served to give somewhat improved light for only a few decades before

'. . . *Procrustean strains beside which ours must appear trifling* . . .'

lamps, as a form as lighting for technological society, became extinct.

Until the beginning of the nineteenth century the rooms of almost everybody in the civilised world were gloomy after dark. Public places and the halls of wealthy people could be made lighter at considerable expense by multiplying the numbers of candles. But these had to be snuffed continually, and dripped and flickered in the draft. Reading and writing in the evenings could only be done by straining one's eyes. Moving about the streets at night was inconvenient and sometimes dangerous. The scientific meetings of the Lunar Society were held when the moon was full because it was more convenient to go out at night then. In Berlin in the early eighteenth century the municipal authorities were forbidden to light the street lamps during the summer months or when the moon was shining in order to save expense.

And then with a rush the wave of technology entirely changed the conditions of life. In the first decade of the nineteenth century gas-lighting arrived, first in London, then in Baltimore, then in Paris, Berlin, Frankfurt and Vienna. This was the beginning of a social revolution. At first some of the British Members of Parliament wore gloves—so as not to burn their fingers—before daring to touch the pipes carrying gas to the lamps newly installed in the debating chamber. But by 1881 this phase of the revolution was almost spent. In that year, Edison demonstrated his electric incandescent bulb at the Paris Exhibition. By the following year, electric light was sweeping gas and petroleum lamps out of the city of New York, and ordinary people were able to enjoy lighting at night that before that time could not have been purchased by royalty.

It would be too far-fetched to suggest that the relative length of the light and dark periods of day and night exerts a biological effect on man similar to that found in sheep, goats, horses, ferrets and chickens. So far as I am aware, there have been no serious scientific investigations of the statistical validity of the assertion that 'in spring the young man's fancy lightly turns to thoughts of love', nor has any evidence been put forward relating the artificial lengthening of the day by means of electric light to changes in human breeding habits. A curious reverse effect is the arbitrary alteration of the diurnal rhythm of whole nations for the purely technological purpose of saving electrical energy.

The idea was started by Mr William Willett in 1906. Willett, a prosperous London builder, started a campaign, which he financed himself, to prove to his fellow countrymen that their industrialised lives and their late nights, artificially prolonged by electric lighting, were corroding their proper enjoyment of living. He declared that people got up one or two hours too late in the summer months. They never experienced the freshness and joy of dewy mornings nor had daylight hours in the evening to spend in natural recreation out of doors. His plan was, therefore, that all clocks should be moved forward four times at regular dates during the spring and summer until they were advanced by a total of eighty minutes. In the autumn they would be moved correspondingly back again.

Willett, though he agitated in Parliament and before expert committees of all sorts, never saw his plan in operation. He died in 1915. But in 1916, the Parliament of Great Britain decreed that the biological rhythm of the forty million British should be modified. The factory workers who started work at 8 o'clock in the morning should in the summer start at 7 o'clock, but in order that there should be no hardship this would be done by calling 7 o'clock 8 o'clock. But it is ironical to reflect that the manœuvre of 'daylight saving', since adopted by numerous countries, from Brazil to Japan, was not done primarily to liberate men's spirits to enjoy the pleasures of nature as William Willett had planned, but rather to economise in electrical power, increase industrial efficiency and maximise engineering output.

It is worth discussing the biological rhythm produced by the light and dark of day and night because of the way in which the animal species we have mentioned, and many others, use it as a part of their biological system. If mankind has adjusted the lighting of day and night to suit his technological environment in one great respect he has as yet done little. I am referring to the breeding habits of the human species.

For most of the hundred thousand years of man's history, human numbers increased only slowly. From the beginnings of man until the Christian era the human population, according to Professor James Bonner of the California Institute of Technology, doubled only about once every 1000 years. This slow rate continued without much change until 300 years ago. Then in the seventeenth century the new thinking of modern science began. Between 1600 and 1800, the world population doubled—that is, in 200 years instead of 1000. And between 1800 and 1900—a hundred years, this time—it doubled again. Now, in our own century, human numbers are doubling each forty years!

The facts of the situation are these. The technology by which we manage our affairs—which provides the D.D.T. to control lice and kill crop pests; the anti-malaria control; the locust control; the systems of plumbing by which we avoid dysentery and typhoid; the vaccines for yellow fever and plague and smallpox; the machines that do the work of a thousand farmers with spades and do it better; the weed control; the improved seeds—all this has been quietly squeezing more and more people into the world. The population of the earth, in fact, is increasing by 1 every second, by 100,000 every day and by 45 million every year. In 1960, there were 2700 million people in the world. By A.D. 2000—a short forty years—this number will, if the present rate continues and no major disasters intervene (such as human suicide, accidental or intentional), be double. That is, there will be 5400 million then.

Until the start of modern science, the human population was kept in check by two potent factors: famine and disease. As long as disease was considered to be beyond the power of man, a punishment from the gods, or due to the spells of one's enemies and the malevolence of witches; and as long as the cultivation of land was taken to be an immutable art learned from one's ancestors, human numbers did not change much from generation to generation. The technological philosophy, first applied in England in the eighteenth and nineteenth centuries, maintained the birth-rate at its previous level while gradually reducing the numbers of people who died in each generation and caused the increasing numbers who did survive to live longer. After two hundred years of British technological effort, the birth-rate has fallen and the number of people has become steady again. A family of ten children is inappropriate in a modern home.

It is quite legitimate to consider human behaviour as a biological phenomenon, in the same way that one observes the behaviour of the camel in the desert, the sheep when moved from one latitude to another where the nights and days are of different length, and the hen exposed to electric lights in its henhouse. Under the circumstances the infliction of technology on the human species can be compared with an epizootic disease, for example, myxomatosis in rabbits.

The most serious of the symptoms of this human contagion is, as we have said, a fall in the death-rate with a consequent increase in numbers. The first human beings to catch the disease were the British and it took them 200 years to attain their present modified immunity; even then they are left with a population of 50 million vastly overcrowding their exiguous island. But biological species can become acclimatised to their afflictions. When the virus of scientific technology swept across Japan, it is true that the population multiplied three-fold before the birth-rate fell to a level approximately in balance with the diminished death-rate. But this time the Procrustean stretching was complete in ninety years, less than half the time taken by the British. The Republic of Mexico represents a community that is at present in the throes of technological infection. The amount of food and crops produced in the country has been increased by sixty per cent in a period of only twenty years. Because there is more to eat and more money to spend, the

Mexican death-rate has come down. The question remains: how soon can the Mexicans get their birth-rate down to balance their falling death-rate. In Ceylon, the same thing is happening: there the death-rate was halved in seven years.

But the camel *can* live in the desert; it has adapted itself to the conditions it finds there. So also can the British and the Japanese live in their restricted islands. True, men are different from camels. The conditions they have to endure came, in the first place, out of their own heads. The adjustment to them has also had to be found in an idea. Camels developed a process by which they became able to allow their temperature to rise and fall; ferrets avoided loosing their young in the rigours of the winter snow by acquiring a sensitivity to the relative duration of light and dark. Men have not had to wait for the process of evolution to change their biological structures to meet the hardships of crowded industrialisation. Instead, after a generation or two, they have used their heads to grasp the idea that economic wealth can only make their children richer if they have fewer of them. In Mexico, intense efforts have been made to apply scientific technology to a previously non-scientific community. Mexico has increased its agricultural productivity more rapidly than any other country in modern times. Agricultural production has increased at a rate of three per cent a year for over twenty years. The Mexicans have devoted an immense effort of intellect to this achievement. But while the productivity of the country has been increasing, the population has been increasing at the same time. Now, there are some intelligent people who are beginning to see that there can be no real hope of their seeing their sons better off for all this effort until the rate of population increase is slowed.

As I mentioned before, the present status of the human population—comprising a growing number of industrially developed countries, usually crowded but with an approximately stable population; a diminishing number of undeveloped countries populated by people who live without benefit of scientific technology whose numbers are kept in check by disease, malnutrition and tribal war; and a further group of nations in a state of transition—is such that the human numbers are doubling every forty years. Professor Bonner has pointed out that if this condition of affairs were to go on for the historically brief period of 700 years, the total number of human beings would be so great that the whole of the dry-land territory of the globe would be covered with people crowded together, standing shoulder to shoulder. But natural behaviour has been proved to be self-correcting. In fully industrialised nations the birth-rate falls. The only problem is, as India and China and Asia and Africa follow Europe and America, whether the check in population increase will come soon enough.

It has been estimated that the maximum number of people that could conceivably be supported on this globe would be about 50,000 million, that is about twenty times as many as there are now. But to feed this absolute maximum would require the full application of every piece of scientific knowledge the human race could deploy: every scrap of cultivable land would need to be cultivated, there would be no place for gardens and playing fields and wastefully distributed houses, and deserts would have to be reclaimed and irrigated with de-salted sea water. The luxury of maintaining extravagant pigs and horses and cats and dogs would have to be abandoned; man would need to eat everything himself.

It is, however, possible to hope that the accelerated rate of recovery from the 'virus' of scientific technology shown by the nations of the globe that successively catch it will continue. Thus, while peoples will inevitably double or triple their populations, it is to be hoped that they will thereafter be able to maintain a stable level. Perhaps, therefore, humanity may possess sufficient continence to call a halt at 8,000 to 10,000 million, which would allow the reasonable comfort of an agricultural efficiency for the whole earth approximately equivalent to that existing in Japan today. If the present half-and-half state of affairs continues, with part of mankind more or less fitted to the Bedstead and part struggling to get in, the human race will know the full force of the Procrustean chopper by the year A.D. 2040 or thereabouts. By then, there will be more people in the world than the earth could support and Procrustes will cut the numbers down.

A society based on scientific technology which is embraced so ardently by the 'advanced' nations of the world possesses many important attractions or we should not be so foolish as to submit ourselves to its inconveniences as eagerly as we do. The fall in the death-rate, for example, although it presents us with serious problems, is in itself admirable. Everyone is in favour of reducing human misery, and the abolition of unnecessary death is an obvious step in that direction. But although the technological framework in which we are now trying to live is the result of intellectual concepts, our behaviour is not influenced solely by intellect. For example, the high fertility that is now causing so much trouble could readily be counterbalanced by technological means. If we put our minds to it, we could easily prevent on a national scale babies being born, but we do not. Can we then learn from other animal species with which we share this earth how to live in harmony with our environment?

The answer seems to be that we can learn some small useful things. We have discussed the camel's methods but their example is little help to man. The French technicians in the Sahara do better by building themselves air-conditioned houses. We learn more from studying sheep. The breeds of sheep best suited to high latitudes, we found, were those which tolerated longer days and shorter nights. Similarly, if the conditions of some human environment demand some special, peculiar qualification—an ability to work at night and sleep by day, for example—we find it is sensible to choose people for that environment who have a physiological aptitude for it. This is the basis of a good deal of modern industrial assessment of fitness.

Perhaps of all the species of biological creation the one that teaches man best how to live without harm in the technological framework that he has built for himself is the tit. This charming bird, that shares so easily with us our town gardens, likes cream. Each morning he watched a sealed bottle of milk arrive on a nearby doorstep. How was he to gain access to it? The ordinary member of the tit species, like the rank and file of man, is not noted for its capacity for original thought, and for some time the aluminium foil cap on the milk bottle presented an impassable obstacle. Then in a single corner of the country there must have appeared a super-tit. Be that as it may, in one small patch the tits learned to puncture the foil cap and drink the cream. Gradually but steadily the progress of enlightenment spread. The area in which the tits knew how to get the milk grew larger and the corresponding territory where a milk bottle was still safe dwindled. Now, throughout the British Isles at least, all the tits have learned how to live contentedly in a technological environment and drink cream, without at the same time losing their natural charm and gaiety and destroying their family life.

10

ALL IN BED TOGETHER

THERE is a moral very applicable to modern life in the story of an Orson Welles broadcast. Visualise the populous cities of the United States, the people in them, rich in technological contrivances: each home with its refrigerator; living-rooms furnished with gadgets of all sorts; the streets filled with motorcars; comfort, food, good clothes, shelter and warmth for all. To an objective observer, these people possessed every material necessity for contentment, and most of them were as content as man can expect to be: on good terms with their wives, with reasonably satisfactory and lucrative jobs, their children being educated and their future tolerably well assured. There were, no doubt, some who were unhappy, poor and sick, but for the main—and taking into account the ordinary pains of the Technological Bedstead that we have been considering for so long—this ought to have been a happy people. But then came Orson Welles, a remarkable man, with that most potent of agents: an idea. And, worse still, he had at his disposal a machine for disseminating ideas broadcast and at the speed of light. I am, of course, referring to the radio. With this machine he caused people all over America to suffer by inflicting on them distress and anxiety which otherwise they would not have felt. He brought home to them the pain of the world— *Weltschmerz*, as the Germans put it.

By broadcasting a play purporting to depict the progress of an invasion from Mars—by painting imaginary details, inventing picturesque accounts of fictitious events, issuing warnings and instructions, filling the air with a pandemonium of contrived alarms, describing invented disasters and relating them to factual situations—Orson Welles, through the exercise of dramatic art and imagination—designed purely for amusement

—preyed on the minds of thousands. Although he was doing this solely by way of wireless telephony, panic swept the community and people ran for their cars and fled through the crowded streets up into the hills. The fact that their alarm and confusion was aroused for a bogus cause—by a dummy made-up fantasy—only emphasises the more the power of the engine by which the thing was done. This was an exceptional example of a commonplace modern force at work. The technological machinery by which instantaneous communication is achieved is part of our environment. In many respects it contributes to our comfort, happiness and convenience. It is useful to be able to lift the telephone and call a taxi; it is comforting to be able to talk at a distance to people of whom we are fond; and it certainly contributes to our felicity and the good life to be able to listen to Beethoven played by a first-rate orchestra whom, but for the intervention of radio broadcasting, it might otherwise not be possible for us to hear. But these benefits have to be paid for. To start with, the development of such means of communication is very new in human history and we have not yet learned how to conform to the newness without hurting ourselves.

The Persians, it is true, invented a system whereby a series of men with loud voices was arranged at strategic intervals across the landscape so that important messages could be transmitted quickly, but this is hardly the same thing as the general diffusion of words and music that now presses so insistently. Even the invention in Greece and Persia—two centuries after the introduction in 600 B.C. of the chain of shouting men—of a series of towers on which torches arranged in a number of different ways spelled out the Greek alphabet could hardly be used for the generalised and individual correspondence that afflicts us today. Indeed, from classical times right up to the French Revolution at the end of the eighteenth century the whole idea of communication over a distance fell into desuetude and people satisfied themselves with the writing of letters, the speed of transmission of which was restricted—as seemed only natural—to the speed of the horse.

All in bed together

The modern age of technology depends as much on the idea of what we feel we would like to do as on our technical ability to do it. The Frenchman, Claude Chappe—described in the books of reference as 'an unemployed priest'—who died in 1805, felt the urge to achieve the technological feat of telegraphy. Possessing no better equipment than the Persians of 600 B.C., or the Greeks, or Shakespeare, or Dr Johnson, he devised a machine consisting of a 17-foot mast with transverse arms that could be moved up and down. In 1795 a message was spelled out on this telegraph and sent 130 miles, being signalled from one to another of sixteen masts erected between Paris and Lille, in a time of two minutes. The civilised world, hungry for technological progress, wondered at the achievement and admired the means by which it had been brought about. The centuries during which people had been content with the post-horse had given place to the thinking of the new age of technology. Soon telegraph towers, with their signal arms out-stretched, gestured their messages from Paris to Rotterdam and Venice. France was criss-crossed by twenty-nine lines of masts. More and more telegraph operators sat all day long with telescopes to their eyes watching for signs of movement in the wooden arms of the next tower in line.

The idea of telegraphy had thus been successful before the modern means by which it is now carried out had been invented. But when the invention had been made and electricity was used for the long-distance transmission of thoughts, the progress of events went forward with a rush. The first message over a wire between two scientists in Göttingen, Gauss and Weber, was in 1833. By 1836, Steinbeil in Berlin devised a telegraph capable of recording its messages on a strip of paper. And when a telegraph was used in London to catch a murderer who was seen boarding a train and who was arrested when he got off at the end of his journey, the usefulness of electric telegraphy as an adjunct to civilised life was assured. It is curious to note that the Chappe telegraph survives to this day in a vestigial form as railway signals.

173

If important, interesting and worthwhile things happen in a distant part of the world it clearly adds to the fulfilment and happiness of our too short lives if we know about them soon. Napoleon was convinced of the virtues of Chappe's wooden semaphore telegraph when in 1809 it brought him the news while he was in Paris that his allies in Bavaria were being attacked by the Austrians. He instantly mounted a counter-attack, surprised the Austrian army and recaptured Munich. Thirty-four years later in 1843, the Congress of the United States became seized with the idea of the usefulness of the electric telegraph in promoting business and voted Samuel Morse $30,000 for the construction of a line from Washington to Baltimore.

The story of the laying of telegraph cables—from Dover to Calais, from England to America, from London to Calcutta—is a romantic narrative of courage and foresight and adventure. The overcoming of setbacks, the persuasion of reluctant backers to continue their support, the loss of broken wires in the depths of the ocean—and their recovery—these narratives contain every element of human behaviour that is admirable. Nevertheless, there are hazards. Man is ringing himself round with voices. The adventurer alone in the desert, the explorer in the loneliness of snow and ice, the sea captain responsible for the ship's company in his charge, John the Baptist solitary in the wilderness—thinking: all these were face to face with a challenge which gives man an opportunity of rising to his full stature. Today, there are few places a man can go to escape the Procrustean pressure of advice, instruction, reproof or distraction—much of it by wire.

It is interesting to recall that in the United States during the period of 'rugged individualism', now long past, the local inhabitants made some attempt to hold back the inroads of technology. The telegraph company would erect their poles and sling the wires from them, whereupon the rural community would cut down the wire and use it for mending fences. It is said also that from time to time shooting matches would be

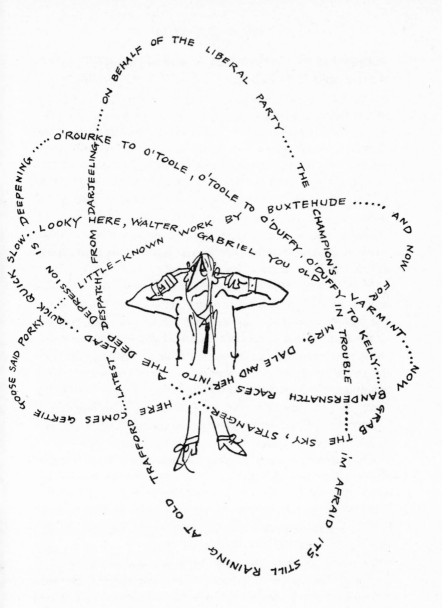

'... *man is ringing himself round with voices* ...'

organised with the glass insulators used as targets. But just as the resistance of the Luddites in England to the introduction of automatic weaving machinery could no more stem the advance of technology than a child's sandcastle can defy the rising tide, so also were the efforts of the American individualists to retain their independent pioneer status futile. It is admirable and useful and socially desirable to be able to catch a criminal by sending a telegram. But if the man happens not to be a criminal, if he happens merely to be eccentric enough not to want to be bothered with up-to-date stock market prices and news of business failures, bankruptcies and the suicides arising therefrom, if he would rather *not* know that the Austrians have invaded Bavaria, there is no escape for him either. The network of wires brings the world of scientific technology into the innermost chamber of his privacy. He is compelled to share the murders, disasters, wars and rumours of war, the tensions of the artificial battles between rival Red Sox and Dodgers, the strained cricket matches between England and Australia, the desperate struggles of Botvinnik to wrest the world chess championship from Tal—all this unsettling *Weltschmerz* he is compelled to suffer because, as a citizen of a technological society, he is inextricably entangled in the telegraph wires and must suffer the consequences.

Of course, the electric telegraph humming and buzzing with the pulses of Samuel Morse's code was only the beginning. In 1876 came the telephone, and it was instantly seized upon as A GOOD THING. No one hesitated to consider whether what was spoken into one end of it was, in fact, worth hearing at the other end. The citizens of the day accepted it as axiomatic that if a material end could be achieved, it was good to achieve it.

The genesis of the telephone represents rather aptly the philosophy of our modern technology. It started with Philipp Reis, a schoolmaster of Friedrichsdorf, who contrived an artificial ear made from a cask-bung covered with a sausage skin to serve as a diaphragm coupled to a knitting-needle wound with wire to form an electric coil. The pressing urge to-ward scientific discovery drove Reis to his death in 1874 at the age of forty, leaving his family in poverty. One of his instruments, however, landed up at Edinburgh University where Alexander Graham Bell was a student. Bell's improved telephone, which was launched in 1876, came to birth in a style characteristic of the age of drive and struggle and headlong technical progress. In fact, Bell was in violent contest with a fellow American, Elisha Gray, whose defeat he achieved at the last instant by registering his application at the patent office two hours ahead of Gray's. This truly was the cut and thrust of the industrial era. But perhaps the most remarkable stroke of poetic justice occurred the following year when Werner Siemens was called in by the Berlin postmaster general to test the new instrument for use in Germany. It was then found that Graham Bell's patents did not extend to that country and the firm of Siemens and Halske thereupon began immediately to mass-produce telephones which they sold at about one tenth the price charged in America.

The telephone is the link between the weak and solitary individual and the protective shelter of the community. When the house is on fire, the telephone will call the fire brigade; the old woman living alone can summon her daughter to help when she falls ill; it provides the weak and helpless with shelter and protection against robbers. But there are also penalties to be borne. The telephone is a measure of technological prosperity. Rich countries—the United States, Sweden—countries to be envied for their technological riches, count their telephones by the million. And citizens of such communities whose personalities conform to the shape of modern prosperity live happily with them.

People whose personalities are different, however, who wish to sit still and think, who would rather concentrate undisturbed on the matter with which they are dealing, do *not* consider that the telephone adds to their happiness. The poet Coleridge was cut off in the middle of his highest flight of poetic creation by a 'person from Porlock' who called on a matter of business.

He never recaptured his poem, and his life, by however small or large an amount, was permanently mutilated. Had the telephone been installed in his house, 'people from Porlock' would, in all probability, have called so insistently that 'Kubla Khan' would never have been started. The technological society, of which the telephone is an integral part, makes little allowance for poets or philosophers. Luckily, most of us soon adapt. We learn to circumvent the insistent ringing of the telephone bell. With practice we become tolerant to breaking a train of thought and subsequently picking it up again. Some adepts have even taught themselves how to continue a coherent conversation with someone who is with them and talk down the telephone at the same time.

There has been a subtle difference between the way radio and, later on, television—both marvels of applied science—have affected our lives and what the telephone has done to us. The telephone bombards us with private voices. There are our business acquaintances, the people who talk about money and commerce and the administration of the industry at which we work. There are the friends who smother us with trivial events, and scandal, and unwanted invitations to uninviting social pleasures. There is the private news of illness and misfortune. Or, sometimes, there are good news and cheerful events. And on a few notable occasions we hear quickly by telephone of things that are valuable and of good repute and worth hearing. Nevertheless, Procrustes uses this machine to play on each one of us separately through the affairs in which we are personally involved.

Radio and television, unlike telephony, exert their influence on our minds and our emotions as a public, not a private, pressure. The boxers on the screen draw out the pugnacity and sophisticated brutality of the community of men who converge, closer and closer, round their cathode tubes. A magician capable of hovering high up over the roofs of a modern city and seeing with his magic eye into a hundred living-rooms would, if an electricity power failure occurred, marvel at the sight of men—and women—suddenly released from the power that had drawn them towards their sets, suddenly relaxing, their motions of sympathetic pugilism checked in mid-stream, re-adjusting their spectacles and returning to the general conversation cut off at the start of the programme.

The telephone is the technological transformation of a private letter. It pushes and pulls us because it rings and rings and must be answered. A letter lies still on the table, we may pick it up or let it lie as we choose. When we read it, we comprehend its message but we need not answer there and then. We are ourselves. We can consider and reflect. The telephone insists; it frets and plucks. You must say something. A letter belongs to the pre-technological age, the telephone is undoubtedly an instrument of Procrustes.

Just as the telephone is a letter—a private message—radio and television represent the Procrustean version of a book. Here is the most immediate and direct avenue to men's minds and, like a book, this modern instrument can be used for diverse purposes, either trivial or serious, good or bad. When a great man can be found to work the machine, to put great ideas into it, Procrustes has an instrument to stretch the intellects of the little people who enjoy the luxuries of his Bedstead. The process of being stretched may not be a comfortable one. The people may hear of great wrongs that they must put right, of harsh decisions that they must take, and of difficult things that they cannot grasp without painful effort. Winston Churchill stretched a whole nation to a stature several sizes larger by speaking through the radio to his countrymen when their arms and equipment were lost, their troops defeated and their confidence destroyed.

These 'mind-machines', radio and television, enrich and refresh people when they open their eyes to new conceptions of beauty and interest, sympathy and knowledge. But Procrustes can, of course, use them as well to cut down and belittle our humanity and civilisation with cheap and vulgar things and the endless repetition of the worthless and the trivial.

The Science Myth

We cannot yet be sure whether this new engine will serve to crush the human spirit more, or whether it will relax some of the existing shackles by which we are already pinned down. We cannot yet see whether the technological possibilities offered by broadcasting will allow the State to dominate the citizens who live in it. Was George Orwell perhaps right about 1984? Administrators with an urge to apply technological methods to the administration of people can do a great deal to render themselves convincing and effective in their television appearances. And they can do much to insure that the impact of what is broadcast shall favour the policy they are working to advance. The remarkable rise of the ungifted and uneducated television 'personality' demonstrates the degree of influence that can be acquired by nonentities and mediocrities. How much more may be wielded by intelligent and ruthless men.

The learned journal *Science* recently discussed methods already used in scientific studies designed to investigate and eventually to control human behaviour. Long-distance television cameras and concealed microphones have been found useful in collecting observations of what people do under various circumstances when they are unaware that they are being observed. There was an instance that acquired some notoriety when, for purely sociological purposes, that is merely to increase the stock scientific knowledge of potential value for technological advance in the future, a jury room was tapped so that the investigators could record by electronic means the behaviour of the jury who believed themselves to be free from observation in a private place.

Microphones and television tubes are machines for projecting ideas; they depend on the technological application of our modern understanding of physics. Because they can be used to influence thoughts and actions of other people, the temptation to do this is often very great. Procrustes will always find nonconformists extremely irritating, to say the least. Surely people who have heterodox opinions about democracy, let us say, or Christianity, or women, should be chopped on the Bedstead until their opinions are cut to measure. It is tempting to apply pressure to compel unconventional Britons to take a proper view of the monarchy or unconvinced Americans to recognise the immorality of unamericanism.

On the other hand, when the newness of the electronic diffusion of ideas has worn off, when we are used to seeing coloured pictures everywhere and news is bounced off the moon as soon as it happens, Theseus may come. He may find some of us before it is too late, release the rack and let us relax to the size we were before our technological communities became so crowded. Before printing was invented, a wise man could write a book for the few people who came to read it. He could teach the pupils who came to hear him. Printing enabled him to broadcast the words he wrote. And now the technical developments of our present age enable him to broadcast the words he speaks as well. When we have become used to the broadcasting machines that we have only had for our own generation, perhaps we shall find a way to use them to see and hear those rare, honourable and wise men whom otherwise we might not know. If Procrustes could arrange this, he would indeed draw us out taller.

These are the two possibilities that are yet to be decided. Whether the machine is used to enable technology to control people, which will certainly be painful to those with original ideas and nonconformist opinions, or whether, on the other hand, radio and television broadcasting will be the technological devices that relax the pinch of industrialisation on modern communities. The democratic freedoms worked best in the gathering in the market place at Athens where the voice of the speaker could reach everyone. At the town meetings of the American pioneer period and in the Swiss cantons people knew one another and had a chance, at least, of understanding the issues they were discussing. The larger numbers, bigger size and increasing complexity of the close-knit technological communities have led to the growth of the impersonal forces by which we are crushed and squeezed. When we have learned to manage our television and radio we may find that they have restored something of the virtues of the Athenian market-place. The ordinary man may get to know the people who work the political machine for him. It is difficult to know what kind of man a speaker is even when he is speaking to us face to face, but after some centuries of practice, the human community has been able to work out a process for assessing whether a man is speaking the truth. It would be very desirable, if it could be done, to carry out a statistical study of the number of times a jury is fooled by the behaviour of the man on trial whom they are trying to judge. But, failing such a study, it is hard to invent a better system than that in which twelve citizens—or fifteen in Scotland—watch his mien and behaviour for the duration of the trial. And if they can sometimes be right about a man accused of having done them harm, they may also be right about a politician who claims to be able to do them good

The process of making up one's mind can, however, be a painful one. Television now brings us all the problems of the world to deal with. Dr Johnson once said that no man ate his dinner with less appetite because of the news of a public misfortune. Today this is no longer quite true. Czechoslovakia could perhaps have been described once upon a time as a distant country of which we knew little. Nowadays, however, news of its military overthrow is spread like a flash and the troubles of the Czechs are our troubles. Before Procrustes came there would have been no need for half the population of the world to keep tortured watch on Captain Kong Lee, General Phoumi Nosovan and Prince Boun Oum, and these men could have been left in their romantic Laotian forests to fight their private war in peace.

The creation of novel and sophisticated desires and their fulfilment through the achievements of modern commerce make life richer and more varied than it has ever been before. The facilities for travel and for the instantaneous communication of ideas have liberated man from the restrictions of his own small plot of ground, And now the greatest achievement of all has been the first flight outside this very planet itself. Technology has indeed provided tinder to light up the spirit of mankind.

And yet it is told that when the hero Theseus was travelling through the Vale of Cephisus he met Procrustes, richly dressed and ornamented. The road was hard and difficult and Procrustes offered him a banquet of venison and wine and told him as well about his wonderful bed, on which tired travellers could sleep as they had never slept before. Theseus, according to the story, was tempted. The wealth and the food and the promised comfort seemed infinitely attractive. And besides, he was anxious to see the gadgetry of the Bedstead. He might have submitted and given up his ambition to be a man and a hero had he not met the old man whose life was spent ceaselessly gathering sticks—the sole individual to fit the bed exactly, to conform perfectly to the machines of life, able to lie lapped in perfect comfort but compelled to devote every waking moment to the interminable business of picking up sticks to keep the Procrustean system going. It was the warning of this dreary old person that impelled Theseus to defiance. Sensibly enough, he gathered up the robber's wealth and treasure and shared it among the people of the country, but just the same he felled Procrustes to the ground 'and his evil soul fled forth, and went down to Hades squeaking, like a bat into the darkness of a cave'. Today our hero has not yet come and Procrustes is very much alive in the modern world. I have tried to describe in this book some of the pains that we are still compelled to suffer in cramming ourselves into the Procrustean Bedstead. To some people, of all the hurts, *Weltschmerz* is the most agonising. *Weltschmerz*—'world-ache'—afflicts us particularly because technology has made the Earth so small. What Prince Boun Oum does today may affect us personally tomorrow if the I.C.B.M.s begin to fly. At a less intense level there are other world ills which concern us very much too. Let an Italian chemist make an incomprehensible discovery in the higher flights of organic chemistry, and the modern streamlined factory down the road, in which so much capital has been invested and which provides agreeable and well-paid employment, may have to close. When Monticatini puts poly-propylene on the market, a shock runs through the poly-ethylene production units all round the world.

'No man is an *Island*, intire of it selfe,' wrote John Donne 300 years ago, 'every man is a peece of the *Continent*, a part of the *maine*.' Today, we know this all too well. When we read of the death of a petty official in the Antipodes our hearts sink with apprehension. Should an unpronounceable cannibal island change hands, the stock markets ten thousand miles away totter in an instant. When Donne wrote, he could justly say, 'if a *Clod* bee washed away by the *Sea*, *Europe* is the lesse, as well as if a *Promontorie* were, as well as if a *Mannor* of thy *friends* or of *thine owne* were'. Today, the whole world is interlocked in a web of technology. Productivity, food supplies, disease, war and peace, all these have become linked throughout the world because of the new power to control distance, communications and things that applied science has provided.

Throughout the world, men are trying to use their new powers for happiness and not for harm. Almost all men in every country are using the same means, the Bedstead. Factories hum, planes fly, telephones ring and words and ideas cross and recross the ether. Mankind has been seized with a single endeavour. Truly, we must take as our own all the world's affairs. Or, as Donne put it, 'I am involved in Mankinde; And therefore never send to know for whom the *bell* tolls; It tolls for *thee*.'

We are all in the Bed together, but we can choose what we are going to do about it. Some may be a good fit: when Productivity says 'work', they work; when Consumption says 'buy', they buy; when The Radio says 'laugh', they laugh. These people may not want to be freed; once their stumps are healed, they enjoy their sleep. Others may suffer themselves to be mutilated or compressed and deformed by the rattling busyness of the technological machinery.

But for some, there may come the spirit of Theseus to give courage to resist. Theseus had as well the wit to see that Procrustes had a substantial treasure, which when distributed to the local inhabitants of the surrounding countryside could give them a better and more enjoyable life. No one of us may be a full-blown hero like Theseus, capable by himself of killing the wicked Procrustes outright, but if we club together some of us may at least give him a fright and even wake up a few of the sleepers as well.

INDEX

Acosta, Joseph, 105
Advertising, 76–95
America and Americans, 2, 36–7,
    65, 67, 81–2, 86, 89, 110,
    128–30, 146, 171, 174, 177, 181
    Army, 43, 73
    Congress, 174
    Federal Trade Commission, 86
    Medical Association, 82, 84–5
Anaesthetics, 103–4
Animals, behaviour of, 154–70
Ardh Kumbh, festival of, 60–4
Assyria, 50–1
    Sennacherib, 50–1
Automation, 1, 16, 26–8

Balding, J., and Hatch, S. H., in-
    vestigations of, 28–9
Banks, Professor Leslie, 60–2
Bantus, 16
Bartlett, Professor Sir Frederick,
    145
Bavaria, 174, 176
Berlin, 173
Biology, Institute of, 16
Boas, Guy, v
Boer War, 40–3
    Battle of Colenso, 40–1
    Fort Wylie, 40–1
Bonner, Professor James, 165
Booth, Dr A., 114
Boun Oum, Prince, 182–3
Boylston, Dr Zabdiel, 101
Bowden, Dr F. P., 75
Boyer, Dr Z., French physician,
    101
Brain Manipulation, 68–73
Britain, Great, 2–3, 6, 16, 36, 67,
    81, 85, 87, 101, 124, 128, 132,
    142–4, 166, 170, 176
    Army, 40–2, 46–9

British people, 36–7, 56, 130–1,
    143, 166–7, 181
    Parliament of, 164
British Association, 106

Calcutta, 174
California Institute of Technology,
    165
Cambridge University, 119
Carson, G., author of *The Corn-
    flake Crusade*, 123–4
Chappe, Claude, 173–4
Churchill, Sir Winston, 179
Clegg, Samuel, 4
Coleridge, S. T., 177–8
Columbia University, 74
Conan Doyle, Sir Arthur, author
    of *The Great Boer War*,
    40–2
Congolese, 17, 42
Cornell University, 99
Crécy, Battle of, 40
Crimean War, 41, 51–2

Darwin, Charles, 106–8
Dickens, Charles, 1, 142
Dingistow, Monmouthshire, 6
Drummond, Sir Jack, v

Edison, Thomas A., 163
Education, 57–9
Elvehjem, Professor C. A., 82
Ergonomics, 32, 44
Eugene VI, Pope, 108

Filiatrault, Abbé, 102–3
Finland and Finns, 17, 128
Fleming, Sir Alexander, 53
Foodstuffs, 15–16, 116–33, 136–7,
    147
Ford, Henry, 10

Index

Index

Index

White, Andrew, author of *A History of the Warfare of Science with Theology in Christendom*, 99
Widdowson, Dr Elsie, 132
Wilberforce, Bishop Samuel, 106
Willett, William, 164
Wilson, Edmund, 2
Wisconsin, University of, 82, 112
Wodehouse, P. G., author of *The Inimitable Jeeves*, 77
Woodward, Joan, 26

World War I, 46–9, 53
  Hulloch Redoubt, 48
  Loos, 47–8
World War II, 43, 45, 52–3, 55, 87, 131

Xerxes, 51
  War against Greece, 51

Yale University, 95, 98

Zinsser, Hans, 51